Long-Term Care

*Understanding Needs
And Options*

Second Edition

America's Health Insurance Plans
Washington, DC 20004

ISBN 1-879143-83-6

Contents

» Tables

America's Health Insurance Plans (AHIP)

This book is published by the Insurance Education Program of America's Health Insurance Plans (AHIP).

AHIP is the national association representing nearly 1,300 member companies providing health insurance coverage to more than 200 million Americans. Our member companies offer medical expense insurance, long-term care insurance, disability income insurance, dental insurance, supplemental insurance, stop-loss insurance, and reinsurance to consumers, employers, and public purchasers.

Our goal is to provide a unified voice for the health care financing industry; to expand access to high-quality, cost-effective health care to all Americans; and to ensure Americans' financial security through robust insurance markets, product flexibility, innovation, and an abundance of consumer choice.

The Insurance Education Program aims to be the leader in providing the highest-quality educational materials and services to the health insurance industry and related health care fields. To accomplish this mission, the program seeks to fulfill the following goals:

- provide tools for member company personnel to use in enhancing the quality and efficiency of services to the public;
- provide a career development vehicle for employees and other health care industry professionals; and
- promote general understanding of the role and contribution of the health insurance industry in the financing, administration, and delivery of health care services.

The Insurance Education Program provides the following services:

- a comprehensive course of study in the fundamentals of health insurance, medical expense insurance, supplemental health insurance, long-term care insurance, disability income insurance, health care management, health care fraud, HIPAA, medical management, and customer service in the health care environment;

- certification of educational achievement by examination for all courses;

- programs to recognize accomplishment in the industry and academic communities through course evaluation and certification, which enable participants to obtain academic or continuing education credits; and

- development of educational, instructional, training, and informational materials related to the health insurance and health care industries.

America's Health Insurance Plans (AHIP)
Insurance Education Program
601 Pennsylvania Avenue, NW
South Building, Suite 500
Washington, DC 20004
800-509-4422
www.insuranceeducation.org
Email:*mgrant@ahip.org*

>> The American Association for Long-Term Care Insurance (AALTCI)

The American Association for Long-Term Care Insurance (AALTCI) is proud to have worked together with AHIP on the development and promotion of the premier designation for the long-term care insurance professional.

AALTCI is a nonprofit professional organization with the singular focus of meeting the needs of long-term care insurance agents, brokers, and insurers.

We invite you to join with thousands of leading LTCI professionals who are members of the association.

For more information on member benefits or a schedule of LTCP classroom review courses, visit our website at *www.aaltci.org*.

The American Association for Long-Term Care Insurance
National Headquarters
3835 East Thousand Oaks Boulevard, Suite 336
Westlake Village, California 91362
818-597-3227
www.aaltci.org
Email: *info@aaltci.org*

Preface

Over the past century, advances in medical science and improvements in living standards have dramatically increased the average life expectancy. Today, most of us can look forward to a long old age. But each of us must also realize that the older we get, the more likely we are to need home health care, nursing home care, or some other form of long-term care assistance. The question is, how will we pay for it?

Many Americans believe that Medicare, the federal health benefits program for the elderly, will cover the cost of long-term care. It will not, nor will Medicare supplement insurance or regular health insurance. Medicaid, the government program for the poor, pays for long-term care, but only if a person is willing to first spend the assets accumulated over a lifetime and become indigent.

Fortunately, planning ahead offers a way of meeting many long-term care needs. For many people, long-term care insurance (LTCI) is a solution to the problem. An LTCI policy provides the assurance that when care is needed, benefits will help cover costs, quality need not be compromised, and assets can be protected.

This book, *Long-Term Care: Understanding Needs and Options*, is an introduction to both long-term care and long-term care insurance. It begins with an explanation of what long-term care is, who needs it, and how and where it is provided. Next, we take a look at various ways of paying for long-term care and the limitations of each. We then examine long-term care insurance, learning how it works and why for many people it is the best solution. The book concludes with a discussion of how insurance salespeople can bring this solution to those who need it and a brief introduction to how insurer home office personnel administer this coverage.

Long-Term Care: Understanding Needs and Options also serves as the textbook for the first of AHIP's four self-study courses in long-term care.

Those completing these courses earn the designation of Long-Term Care Professional (LTCP); the first course can also be chosen as an elective by those pursuing the Health Insurance Associate (HIA) designation.

The book has been written and organized to make concepts and information easy to learn and to facilitate study and review. Key terms are in boldface and are marked in the margin with this symbol: ⬛━. There are review questions at the end of each chapter. And throughout the text there are exercises designed to engage readers in active learning and help them deepen and expand their knowledge through research.

AHIP hopes that *Long-Term Care: Understanding Needs and Options* will not only serve as a resource for those in the insurance industry, but that it will also help those from other fields and consumers understand the need for long-term care that we all face and must plan for.

Note to the second edition: New forms of long-term care, including new services and settings, are continuously being developed in order to provide people with the best care possible while maximizing their independence and enjoyment of life. Long-term care insurance is also evolving, as insurance companies create innovative product features in an effort to better meet the needs of consumers and respond to changes in government programs and regulations. This second edition of *Long-Term Care: Understanding Needs and Options* has been extensively revised to reflect the developments of recent years as well as ongoing trends. And as the field continues to evolve, AHIP will frequently update our textbooks to provide readers with the most accurate and current information. Readers should also visit AHIP's web site (*www.ahip.org*) for the latest developments.

Gregory F. Dean, JD, CLU, ChFC, LTCP
Executive Director, Insurance Education Program
America's Health Insurance Plans

This book is intended for educational purposes. Its contents are not a statement of policy. The views expressed or suggested in this and all other AHIP textbooks are those of the contributing authors and are not necessarily the opinions of AHIP or of its member companies.

This book is sold with the understanding that AHIP is not engaged in rendering legal, accounting, tax, or any other professional service. If legal advice or other expert assistance is required, the services of a professional should be sought.

It should be kept in mind that the insurance industry is continuously changing and the information in this or any book may be superseded by the latest trends and innovations. For information on current developments, the reader should visit AHIP's web site at *www.ahip.org* and the AALTCI web site at *www.aaltci.org*.

» Acknowledgments

Contributors and Reviewers

Cathi-Lynne Ames
Prudential

L. Sue Andersen
Health Benefits ABCs

Margie Barrie, CSA, LTCP
Hagelman Barrie Sales Training Solutions

Judith Bass, MHP, FLMI, ACS, HIA, ALHC, LTCP
State Farm Insurance

Sharil L. Baxter, MSM, CLTC, LTCP, CSA, MHP, RHU
MetLife Investors

David Brenerman
UnumProvident Corporation

Marie Bucci, CLTC
John Hancock Life Insurance Company

Brian Burwell
Thomson Medstat

Winthrop S. Cashdollar
America's Health Insurance Plans

Timothy P. Cassidy
Long Term Care Group, Inc.

Susan A. Coronel
America's Health Insurance Plans

Steffani M. Crawley
AEGON Insurance Group

Harry Crosby, LTCP
Genworth Financial

John Cutler, Esq.
U.S. Office of Personnel Management

Gregory F. Dean, JD, CLU, ChFC, LTCP
America's Health Insurance Plans

Janice Dimon, HIA, LTCP
Metropolitan Life Insurance Company

Dave Donchey, CLU, LTCP
Leisure Werden and Terry

Phyllis Felser
Felser Insurance Services, LLC

Angie Forsell
Long Term Care Group, Inc.

Carol Gardner
LifeStyle Insurance Services, Inc.

Rachel Gawthorp, RN, CMC, LTCP
State Farm Insurance

Robert P. Glowacki, FLMI, CLU
AEGON Insurance Group

Jason G. Goetze
Northwestern Mutual

Jocelyn F. Gordon, Esq.
LifePlans, Inc.

Dave Gregg
Mutual of Omaha

Allen Hamm
Superior LTC Insurance Agency, Inc.

Andrew E. Hanson
Hanson Financial Services

Patrick E. Hoesing
Art Jetter and Company

Edward S. Hutman, CLTC
Comprehensive LTC Group, LLC

Arthur C. Jetter, Jr., CLU, CFP, RHU, FLMI, REBC, LTCP
Art Jetter and Company

Roy W. Kern, LUTCF, CLTC, CSA, RFC
Roy W. Kern and Associates

Jim Knotts, FLMI, FLHC, HIA, ACS
State Farm Insurance

Diane Lavin
Metropolitan Life Insurance Company

Sally H. Leimbach, CLU, CEBS
LTC Insurance Specialists, LLC

Maureen Lillis
CHCS Services

Terry Lowe, HIA, CLU, ChFC, FMLI, FLHC, ACS
State Farm Insurance

Beth M. Ludden, FLMI, LTCP
New York Life Insurance Company

Joelyn Malone, MA
Malone Consulting

Marcia A. Marshall
Severn Avenue Group Consulting

Christine McCullugh
LTC Solutions, Inc.

Hunter McKay
U.S. Department of Health and Human Services

Deirdre A. McKenna, JD
American Council of Engineering Companies

Joan Melanson
Long-Term Care Partners, LLC

Anthony Monderine
Bankers Life and Casualty Company

Sam Morgante
Genworth Financial

Nancy P. Morith, CLU, LTCP, CSA
NP Morith, Inc.

Raymond Nelson, ASA, MAAA
Bankers Life And Casualty Company

Debra C. Newman, CLU, ChFC, LTCP
Newman Long-Term Care

Ann Gillespie Pietrick, JD
Conseco Services, LLC/Bankers Life and Casualty Company

Howard H. Russell, EdD
Human Assets Group

Lee Sacks, CLTC, CSA
Daniel Charles, Inc.

Abe Scher, MSW, LCSW
Scher Long-Term Care Insurance Services, Inc.

Beth Singley
Assisted Living Federation of America (ALFA)

J. Eugene Tapper, MS, NHA
Glocal Insurance Marketing

Eileen J. Tell, MHP
Long Term Care Group, Inc.

Michael Thresher
J. T. Ryan and Associates

Sandra Timmermann, ED
MetLife Mature Market Institute

Karen A. Wayne
Assisted Living Federation of America (ALFA)

William C. Weller, FSA, MAAA
Omega Squared of Sedona, Inc.

Thomas Wildsmith, HIA, MHP, FSA, MAAA, CLU, ChFC, FLMI
Hay Group, Inc.

General Reviewers

Nancy P. Morith, CLU, LTCP, CSA
NP Morith, Inc.

Eileen J. Tell, MHP
Long Term Care Group, Inc.

Editors

Michael G. Bell
Consulting editor

Howard H. Russell, EdD
Human Assets Group

1

Long-Term Care: An Overview

> - What Is Long-Term Care?
> - When Is Long-Term Care Needed?
> - The Growing Need for Long-Term Care
> - Long-Term Care Services and Settings

» What You Will Gain from This Chapter

As a result of the reading, research, and thinking you do in this chapter, you will be able to explain what long-term care is and describe the indicators of a person's need for long-term care, the growing need for long-term care in the United States, and where and how long-term care is delivered.

» What Is Long-Term Care?

Long-term care is a broad range of services provided over a prolonged period, the purpose of which is to minimize or compensate for a person's loss of physical or mental functioning resulting from an illness, disability, cognitive impairment (such as Alzheimer's disease), or simply the frailties of old age.

To understand long-term care, it is helpful to understand how it differs from **acute care**:

- Acute care is a medical intervention lasting a relatively short time. Acute care is intended to treat or cure an individual with a critical illness or injury and restore previous levels of functioning. Acute care is provided by physicians, nurses, and other medical professionals, and it normally takes place in a hospital.

- Long-term care, unlike acute care, is not primarily intended to cure or treat a medical condition. Instead, it focuses on coping with a person's reduced level of physical or cognitive functioning over an extended period, sometimes indefinitely. Some long-term care services are rendered by health care professionals such as nurses and therapists, but long-term care is more often provided by nonprofessional personnel such as home health aides, or by informal caregivers such as family and friends.

Coping with a person's reduced level of functioning, the focus of long-term care, can include medical treatment, skilled nursing care, and therapy of various sorts. But it more typically involves assisting a person with the following:

- basic functions, such as bathing, dressing, getting out of bed, going to the toilet, and eating;
- household chores, such as meal preparation and cleaning;
- life management, such as shopping, money management, and taking medications; and
- transportation.

Long-term care can take place in a number of different settings. These include nursing homes, residential facilities (such as assisted living residences), community-based facilities (such as adult day centers), or the home of the person receiving care. And as mentioned above, long-term care is provided by a variety of individuals, including health care professionals such as nurses or therapists (who provide **skilled care**) as well as nonprofessional personnel, family, and friends (who provide **personal care**—that is, assistance with basic living functions and household chores).

To read more on the definition of long-term care, visit the web site of America's Health Insurance Plans (AHIP), *www.ahip.org*. Go to the "Consumer Information" section, click on the "Guide to Long-Term Care Insurance," and read the first section, "What Is Long-Term Care?" You can download the AHIP guide from the web site, or you can order copies through the Federal Citizen Information Center by calling 888-8PUEBLO (888-878-3256) (order item #331M, $1.00 each). Bulk orders of the guide are

Research

available to financial services and insurance professionals through the Life and Health Insurance Foundation for Education (LIFE) at *www.life-line.org/catalog* or by calling 800-268-7680.

You may want to use a search engine to locate other definitions of long-term care on the Internet.

Thinking

Based on what you already knew and what you have learned about long-term care from your reading and research, write down what you would say to help someone understand what long-term care is.

_____

_____

_____

_____

_____

_____

_____

_____

» When Is Long-Term Care Needed?

Whether a person needs long-term care and what care he or she needs is determined by a health care professional. An important part of the process is an assessment of the person's ability to perform simple, everyday activities. There are two sets of such activities that are generally assessed—activities of daily living and instrumental activities of daily living.

The **activities of daily living (ADLs)** are basic activities that a person must be able to perform to take care of herself. The inability to perform ADLs is the most reliable and objective indicator of the need for long-term care services. The following six ADLs are commonly used to assess this need:[1]

- bathing—washing oneself by sponge bath or in either a tub or shower (including getting into and out of the tub or shower);
- dressing—putting on and taking off all clothing items and any necessary braces, fasteners, or artificial limbs;
- toileting—getting to and from the toilet, getting on and off the toilet, and performing associated personal hygiene;
- transferring—moving into or out of a bed, chair, or wheelchair;
- continence—being able to maintain control of bowel and bladder function or, when unable to maintain control, being able to perform associated personal hygiene (including caring for catheter or colostomy bag); and
- eating—feeding oneself by getting food into the body from a receptacle such as a plate, cup, or table, or by a feeding tube or intravenously.

These ADLs are listed above in the order in which people lose the ability to perform them. This order is very predictable, and interestingly, it is exactly the reverse of the order in which children acquire the ADLs. For instance, eating (picking up food and putting it in the mouth) requires only gross motor skills and a limited range of motion. It is the first ADL children acquire and the last adults lose. In contrast, bathing and dressing are very complex tasks that require fine motor skills (to manage buttons and zippers), balance (to stay on one leg while putting on pants), and an extended range of motion (to reach back to pull on a sleeve). These are the last ADLs children acquire and the first adults lose.

In some cases, a person is physically independent and able to perform all activities of daily living but still needs long-term care because of a **cognitive impairment**, a condition (such as Alzheimer's disease) that causes a substantial diminishment of reasoning, intellectual capacity, or memory and results in confusion, disorientation, impaired judgment, or memory loss. Individuals with these disorders need supervision to ensure their health and safety and may or may not also need help with ADLs.

An early indication of the possible need for long-term care is difficulty in performing **instrumental activities of daily living (IADLs)**, activities a person must be able to do in order to function independently in the community. IADLs include the following:[2]

- grocery shopping,
- meal preparation,
- laundry,
- housework or handyman work,
- using the telephone,
- getting to places beyond walking distance,
- managing medication, and
- managing money.

» The Growing Need for Long-Term Care

Concern about long-term care is growing as the population in need of such care increases. This increase is largely a result of the greater numbers of elderly people in our society. It is true that not all of those in need of long-term care are old, but it is also true that as people grow older the need for assistance with activities of daily living increases significantly. For example, as of 1999, those age 75 or older were more than three times likelier to have an ADL limitation than those age 65 to 74.[3]

Thus as the elderly population grows, the need for long-term care increases. And in the United States today, the elderly population is increasing rapidly both in numbers and as a proportion of the total population. For example, in 2000 individuals age 65 and older made up just under 13 percent of the population; by 2030 this figure is projected to increase to almost 20 percent.[4]

This increase in the number of elderly persons results in part from people living longer because of improvements in living standards and advances in medical science. In 1900 the average life expectancy was 47 years; for those born in 1950 (who will turn 65 in 2015), the average life expectancy is 68 years; and those born in 1999 can expect to live to the age of 77 on average.[5]

Another cause of the growth of the elderly population is the aging of the baby boom generation. The more than 76 million baby boomers born between 1946 and 1964 form a bulge in the U.S. population, and in 2011 these people will begin turning 65.

In summary, the elderly have become our society's fastest-growing age group, and as a result, the need for long-term care is growing rapidly. In fact, many experts question whether our current delivery and financing system will be able to adequately cope with the sheer numbers likely to require long-term care in the future.

Go to the web site of the National Center for Health Statistics, *www.cdc.gov/nchs*, and see what you can find out about the growing need for long-term care among aging Americans. The "Aging" section under "Initiatives" is a good place to begin looking. You also might see what is in the "News Releases and Fact Sheets" sections.

Write how you would explain the growing need for long-term care in the United States.

» Long-Term Care Services and Settings

Today, thanks to new technology and new arrangements for care, there is a wide variety of settings in which long-term care can be delivered. Improved technology means that services once provided only in hospitals and nursing homes can now be delivered at home or elsewhere. Innovative care settings include assisted living residences, adult day centers, and others. In the remainder of this chapter, we will look at the many long-term care services and settings.

Long-Term Care at Home

For most people, home is the preferred setting for long-term care. Remaining at home reinforces a person's sense of independence. The person can maintain her accustomed habits and daily routines. Surroundings are familiar, and accumulated possessions call to mind lifetime memories. For someone with diminishing cognitive abilities, this familiar environment can provide "cues" for cognition, and a person with reduced physical functioning can arrange her own home in way that makes coping with her particular limitations easier. In contrast, a nursing home resident lives in an unfamiliar place and must usually follow institutional regimens. And indeed, most people receive long-term care at home, rather than in a facility.

Traditionally, home care meant that a person was taken care of by a family member, usually a woman who was not employed outside the home. The elderly person either moved in with his **family caregiver** or was visited by her in his own home several times a day. However, this situation is becoming less common, as a majority of women in the United States now have full-time or part-time jobs. Today, while most family caregivers are still female, almost 40 percent are male.[6]

Still, many women and men with jobs also provide care to aged or disabled family members. Indeed, 59 percent of family caregivers are employed, most (48 percent) full-time.[7] But caring for a person with a severe functional impairment at home can be overwhelming. While almost half of all family caregivers report spending no more than eight hours per week on caregiving, one-fourth spend more than 20 hours, and for 17 percent it is a full-time job, consuming more than 40 hours a week.[8]

Family members who help elderly people with a severe disability also face a higher risk of serious illness and mortality themselves. Over one-third of those meeting the highest caregiving demands experience physical and mental problems as a result of caregiving, and they describe their own health status as only fair or poor. And over one-third of all caregivers report an emotional stress level of four or five on a five-point scale (where five is "very stressful").[9] For those who are also raising children (just under 40 percent of all family caregivers[10]), the burden is particularly great. These members of the "sandwich generation" often feel caught between the care of their children and the care of their parents, not to mention the demands of their jobs. They often find that they have too many responsibilities to meet and too many needs to satisfy.

In summary, most people hope to avoid entering a nursing home and want to live as independently as possible in their own homes or some other homelike setting for as long as they can. At the same time, family caregivers, who often make continued residence at home possible, are frequently overwhelmed by the demands of providing care. In response to this problem, a new approach to long-term care has developed, called **aging in place**. Aging in place means that the person stays at home, and needed services are provided there or in the community. These services help the person avoid entering a nursing home and ease the burden on family caregivers. Aging in place is made possible by the following:

- **home health care providers**, which provide nursing care, personal care, home health aide care, therapy, and homemaker/chore services;

- **community-based care**, which includes adult day centers, senior centers, and congregate meal sites, as well as transportation services and home-delivered meals; and

- **residential care**, which allows the elderly to maintain their own independent living spaces while also having access to needed personal care and household support services. This includes assisted living residences and continuing care retirement communities.

These services and facilities, as well as nursing homes, are described below.

Home Health Care Providers

Many families call on a home health care provider when a person needing care prefers to stay at home but requires services that cannot easily or effectively be provided solely by family and friends. Home health care agencies serve recovering, disabled, chronically ill, terminally ill, and cognitively impaired persons, and they deliver at home a wide range of services, including medical, nursing, or therapeutic treatment; assistance with the activities of daily living; and supervision. There is also a growing number of independent home health care providers—nurses, therapists, and home health aides who provide similar care and services but who are not affiliated with an agency. Some states certify or license these independent providers.

A physician, care manager, hospital discharge planner or social services coordinator, or a local Area Agency on Aging can help families locate home care providers in their area. State departments of health, aging, or social services can provide a list of licensed home health care agencies. In evaluating providers, family members should always ask questions and choose carefully, taking into consideration the following issues:

- How long has the provider been in business?
- Can the provider supply references?
- Does the provider supply literature explaining its services, eligibility requirements, fees, and funding sources?
- Are the patient's home care needs evaluated by a nurse or therapist?
- Does the provider include the patient and her family members in developing a plan of care?
- Is the patient's course of treatment documented, detailing specific tasks of the provider?
- How does the provider select and train its employees?
- Does the provider assign supervisors to oversee the quality of care?
- What procedures does the provider have in place to handle emergencies?
- How does the provider bill for services?
- How does the provider ensure patient confidentiality?
- Is an independent provider licensed or certified (if this is required by the state in which he is practicing)?
- Can an independent provider demonstrate that he is qualified by training and experience, and can he provide references?

The above questions are based on a list appearing on the web site of the National Association for Home Care, *www.nahc.org*. Go to that site and browse to find more information. Click on "Consumers" on the menu to the left of the screen to get to the guidelines on how to choose a home care provider.

Adult Day Centers

Adult day centers have become an increasingly popular way of providing community-based assistance in meeting the needs of functionally or cognitively impaired adults. These centers run on the same principles as day care for children. They are open during customary business hours, allowing caregivers to work during the day and care for their family member during evenings and weekends. They provide supervision, personal care, help with managing medications, and other supportive services. A variety of social, recreational, and educational activities may also be offered to participants. Many are run by nonprofit agencies, and the cost is sometimes based on the ability to pay.

Respite Care

Respite care is long-term care provided during a limited period for the purpose of giving a family caregiver a break. The period may be for a few hours so that the caregiver can take care of personal business, or it may be for several days to allow him to take a vacation or just relax. Respite care is provided by home health care agencies, independent home care providers, assisted living residences, and nursing homes for a fee. There may also be community-based services that provide respite care on an informal basis in homes.

Given what you have learned about home care and the support available to family caregivers from your reading and research, write down what you would say to explain to someone the home care options available to them.

Thinking

_____

_____

_____

_____

_____

_____

_____

_____

_____

Nursing Homes

Nursing homes (also called **skilled nursing facilities** or **convalescent care facilities**) provide a wide range of services, including 24-hour nursing care, supervision, assistance with ADLs, and rehabilitative services such as physical, occupational, and speech therapy. Some people stay in them for a short period of recovery and/or rehabilitation after a serious illness or operation and then return home. But the traditional role of these facilities is providing long-term care for the chronically ill or disabled. Typically, families seek nursing home care when a relative's condition reaches the point where it is no longer possible to safely care for him at home, even with professional help, or when the cost of round-the-clock care at home becomes too great.

Nursing homes are highly regulated. They must be licensed by state governments, and in order to receive Medicaid and Medicare benefits, they must also be certified by those programs. Licensure and certification are intended to ensure that residents are cared for in a safe physical environment and that they receive high-quality care from qualified providers, and regulators closely monitor facilities. However, quality can and does vary from one nursing home to another.

There are some guidelines that can help a family select a facility. The family should obtain basic information about the facility. They should ask to see the current licenses of the facility and its administrator, and they should ask the following questions:

- Is the facility Medicare and Medicaid certified, and does it accept other forms of insurance?
- What is the daily rate, what does this daily rate cover, and are there any additional fees for laundry, supplies, medication, therapy, or other services?
- Are there any vacancies? If not, are vacancies anticipated, and how long is the waiting list?

The family should inspect the facility and ascertain the following:

- Is the facility clean and odor-free throughout?
- Is the facility well-lighted and homelike in both common spaces and private quarters?

■ Does each resident have ample closet space, a comfortable chair, a reading light, and a locked drawer with a key?

■ Does every room have a window?

■ Are private telephones and televisions allowed?

■ Is there a working call-bell at each bed, toilet, and bathing area?

■ Are the common areas of the facility wheelchair accessible, and are the lavatories conveniently located?

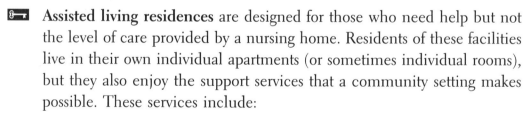

The Medicare "Nursing Home Compare" web site, *www.medicare.gov/NHCompare/*, is a good place to get more information about nursing homes. The site allows you to search for nursing homes by name, within a certain geographic area, or based on other criteria. At *www.medicare.gov* you will also find articles providing general information and advice on selecting a nursing home. Information about finding a nursing home or assisted living residence is also available at *www.longtermcareliving.com*.

Assisted Living Residences

Assisted living residences are designed for those who need help but not the level of care provided by a nursing home. Residents of these facilities live in their own individual apartments (or sometimes individual rooms), but they also enjoy the support services that a community setting makes possible. These services include:

■ up to three meals a day;

■ assistance with personal care;

■ help with medications, housekeeping, and laundry services;

■ 24-hour onsite staff to respond to emergencies; and

■ social programs.

Facilities of this type are known by many different names. Their cost also varies widely depending on geographic area, the size of the community, the services offered, and other factors. Assisted living residences are regulated in all states, but states' requirements vary.

Several web sites have information on selecting an assisted living residence: One is the site of the Assisted Living Federation of America (ALFA), *www.alfa.org.* In addition, "A Consumer Guide to Assisted Living and Residential Care Facilities" can be found at *www.longtermcareliving.com/planning_ahead/assisted/ assisted1.htm.* While you are at these sites, browse for additional information about assisted living. Also visit the web site for the Center for Excellence in Assisted Living, *www.theceal.org.*

Continuing Care Retirement Communities (CCRCs)

Continuing care retirement communities (CCRCs), sometimes called **life care communities**, offer several levels of care in one location. For example, many CCRCs offer independent housing (for those who need little or no supportive care or services), assisted living housing, and a nursing home, all on one campus. An individual can obtain different services as his needs change, without having to move to a new community. Thus a resident who loses his ability to live independently can move from the independent area to the assisted living area, or he can receive home care in his living unit. And if the resident's condition worsens, he can enter the onsite nursing home.

The web site of the American Association of Retired Persons (AARP), *www.aarp.org,* is a good place to get information about CCRCs and advice on choosing one. Enter "CCRC" in the search box and click on "Go." While you are there, familiarize yourself with the other resources on the AARP site.

Adult Foster Care

Adult foster care is much like foster care for children. Elderly adults who need help functioning or who cannot live safely on their own live with a foster family. Foster families provide room and board as well as 24-hour supervision and assistance with ADLs, either to an individual or a small group. Sometimes those receiving care pay for these services. In other instances, a government program pays for foster care. State licensure of this type of facility, as well as the terminology used for it, vary greatly.

Board and Care Home

Board and care homes (also called **residential care facilities**) are usually small residential facilities, with 20 or fewer residents. Residents receive all meals as well as personal care and 24-hour protective oversight. They are not appropriate for individuals who need the level of care available in a nursing home, since nursing and medical attention are usually not provided on the premises. As with adult foster care, terminology and state licensure vary greatly.

Hospice Care

Hospice care provides services and support for the dying and their families. Usually, hospice patients have a life expectancy of six months or less. The purpose of hospice care is not primarily to treat the medical condition of the patient, which is incurable, but rather to improve the quality of life for the time that remains. Care focuses on pain and symptom management, social services, and emotional and spiritual support for the terminally ill and their families.

Hospice care may be provided in the patient's home or in a facility. Care is provided by a team that includes registered nurses, licensed professional nurses, home health aides, social workers, therapists, chaplains, and bereavement counselors. Volunteers are also involved. Hospice services are generally fully or partially covered by Medicare, Medicaid, private insurers, and prepaid health plans.

Research
A source of information on long-term care resources in your area is the local Area Agency on Aging or Council on Aging. Look it up in the phone book and call for an appointment to visit with the director. This office should be able to give you a directory of long-term care organizations and information on costs in your area.

After you have done your reading and research, write down what you would do and say to help someone find the appropriate long-term care setting for a family member in your area.

Thinking 💡

_____

_____

_____

_____

_____

_____

_____

_____

_____

» What's Next

In the next chapter, we will survey ways people expect to pay for long-term care—private savings and assets, family assistance, the Medicare and Medicaid programs, and various forms of private insurance. In the following chapters, we will examine these alternatives in greater depth.

Key Terms 🔑

Activities of daily living (ADLs)

Acute care

Adult day center

Adult foster care

Aging in place

Assisted living residence

Board and care home

Cognitive impairment

Community-based care

Continuing care retirement community (CCRC)

Convalescent care facility

Family caregiver

Home health care provider

Hospice care

Instrumental activities of daily living (IADLs)

Life care community

Long-term care   Respite care
Nursing home   Skilled care
Personal care   Skilled nursing facility
Residential care

» Review Questions

1. What is long-term care?

2. What are the major distinctions between acute care and long-term care?

3. Who provides skilled care? Who provides personal care?

4. What are the activities of daily living (ADLs)? What are the instrumental activities of daily living (IADLs)?

5. What is a cognitive impairment?

6. What are some community-based services in the area of long-term care?

7. What types of services do home care providers offer?

8. How does an adult day center help a family caregiver cope?

9. How does respite care help a family caregiver cope?

10. What services are provided in a nursing home?

11. What is an assisted living residence?

12. What is a continuing care retirement community (CCRC)?

13. What is adult foster care?

14. What is a board and care home?

15. What is the purpose of hospice care?

» Answers

1. A broad range of services provided over a prolonged period, the purpose of which is to minimize or compensate for a person's loss of physical or mental functioning resulting from an illness, disability, cognitive impairment (such as Alzheimer's disease), or simply the frailties of old age.

2. Acute care is intended to treat or cure an individual with a critical illness or injury and restore previous levels of functioning; long-term care focuses on coping with a person's reduced level of functioning. Acute care is provided by physicians, nurses, and other medical professionals; long-term care is usually provided by nonprofessional personnel such as home health aides, or by informal caregivers such as family and friends. Acute care lasts a relatively short time; long-term care is provided over an extended period, sometimes indefinitely.

3. Health care professionals such as nurses and therapists provide skilled care; nonprofessional personnel, family, and friends provide personal care.

4. The activities of daily living are basic activities that a person must be able to perform to take care of herself; the instrumental activities of

daily living are activities a person must be able to do in order to function independently in the community.

5. A condition (such as Alzheimer's disease) that causes a substantial diminishment of reasoning, intellectual capacity, or memory and results in confusion, disorientation, impaired judgment, or memory loss.

6. Adult day centers, senior centers, congregate meal sites, transportation services, and home-delivered meals.

7. Nursing care, personal care, home health aide care, therapy, and homemaker/chore services.

8. They are open during customary business hours, allowing caregivers to work during the day and care for their family member during evenings and weekends.

9. Respite care allows a family caregiver to take a break, which may last a few hours so that he can take care of personal business or several days so he can take a vacation or just relax.

10. Twenty-four-hour nursing care, supervision, assistance with ADLs, and rehabilitative services such as physical, occupational, and speech therapy.

11. A long-term care facility in which residents live in their own individual apartments (or sometimes individual rooms) but also have support services available.

12. A community that offers several levels of long-term care (such as independent housing, assisted living, and a nursing home) in one location.

13. In adult foster care elderly adults who need help functioning or who cannot live safely on their own live with a foster family that provides room and board as well as 24-hour supervision and assistance with ADLs.

14. A small residential facility in which residents receive all meals as well as personal care and 24-hour protective oversight.

15. To improve the quality of life of the terminally ill for the time that remains, with a focus on pain and symptom management, social

services, and emotional and spiritual support for patients and their families.

NOTES

1 Katz, S., Amasa, A. B., Roland, W., Jackson, B. A., and Jaffe, M. W. 1963. "Studies of Illness in the Aged: The Index of ADLs." *Journal of the American Medical Association* 183(12): 914-919.

2 Lawton, M. P., and Brody, E. M. 1969. "Assessing Older People: Self-Maintaining and Instrumental Activities of Daily Living." *Gerontology* 9:179-186.

3 U.S. Department of Health and Human Services, Centers for Disease Control and Prevention, National Center for Health Statistics. 2001. *Health, United States, 2001*; special excerpt: "Trend Tables on 65 and Older Population," p. 236.

4 U.S. Department of Commerce, Bureau of the Census. 2004. "Projected Population of the United States, by Age and Sex, 2000 to 2050."

5 U.S. Department of Health and Human Services, Centers for Disease Control and Prevention, National Center for Health Statistics. 2001. *Health, United States, 2001*; special excerpt: "Trend Tables on 65 and Older Population," p. 163.

6 National Alliance for Caregiving and AARP. April 2004. *Caregiving in the U.S.*

7 Ibid.

8 Ibid.

9 Ibid.

10 Ibid.

Paying for Long-Term Care

» What You Will Gain from This Chapter

As a result of the reading, research, and thinking you do in this chapter, you will be able to describe the costs of long-term care and discuss the ways people expect to pay those costs.

» The Cost of Long-Term Care

The cost of long-term care varies according to the service provided and the geographic location. In 2004 the average annual cost of nursing home care in the United States was just under $62,000, or about $169 per day for a semiprivate room. The cost of a private room averaged $192 per day, with local costs ranging from a low of $87 in Louisiana to a high of $435 in Alaska.[1] This means that the average nursing home stay (approximately two and a half years[2]) in a semiprivate room could cost almost $155,000. As for long-term care provided at home, the average cost of a home health care aide in 2004 was $18 per hour, with a range of $13 to $28 according to location.[3]

Naturally, as a result of inflation long-term care costs will continue to rise. Based on a national index of long-term care cost increases (similar to the Consumer Price Index), the price of long-term care services has risen by about 5 percent annually in recent years.[4] And the impact of inflation is important to consider in planning for the future. For example, it is estimated that the cost of long-term care will rise dramatically by 2030, when the last of the baby boomers have reached 65. In 2030 a visit from a licensed professional home health provider could cost $220, an annual stay in an assisted living residence could start at $109,300, and the yearly cost of a nursing home could be $190,600.[5]

Research

Find out the range of cost for the following types of long-term care in your area:

- home health care,
- adult day centers,
- assisted living, and
- nursing home care.

You can get this information from your local Area Agency on Aging or Council on Aging. This office should be able to give you a directory of long-term care services and information on costs in your area. Another way is to go to the Yellow Pages, look up providers and facilities listed under the above categories, and ask them about costs.

Thinking

After you have done your reading and research, write down what you would say to help someone in your area understand the range of costs a person should be prepared to pay for each of the various long-term care services.

_____

_____

_____

_____

_____

_____

_____

» Ways of Paying for Long-Term Care

Long-term care costs are often paid directly out of pocket by individuals or their families when services are needed. This happens because people often don't understand the need to make other arrangements until it is too late, and because they don't know that long-term care is not generally covered by private health insurance, disability insurance, Medicare, or other common benefit sources.

There are seven principal sources of funding that people may expect to draw on to pay for long-term care. Not all of these apply to every person, and they vary significantly in terms of whether, when, and how they may be relied on. They are:

- personal savings and other financial assets,
- help from family members,
- the Medicare program,
- private Medicare supplement insurance (called MedSupp or Medigap insurance),
- private health insurance and disability income insurance,
- the Medicaid program, and
- long-term care insurance (LTCI).

In this chapter, we will briefly survey these options, and in the following chapters we will look at each of them in more depth.

» Savings and Assets

While most people who pay for long-term care out of their own funds do so simply because they have made no other arrangements and have no alternative, some individuals consciously plan to use their own savings and assets to pay for care. Those planning to take this approach should consider these questions:

- Will your accumulated assets be sufficient to cover your long-term care needs?
- Even if your accumulated assets are enough, do you really want to spend them on long-term care? Wouldn't you prefer to preserve them and pass them on to your spouse or other heirs?

As we have seen, long-term care services are extremely expensive, and paying for them requires a large amount of assets. Suppose, for example, that someone who is 45 years old today decides to create a fund to pay for her future long-term care needs. As mentioned above, the average length of stay in a nursing home is roughly 2.5 years; if we assume an average cost of $160 per day, the total amount at today's costs will be $146,000. And if the person requires that amount of nursing home care in 40 years when she is 85, she will need $1,027,839 (accounting for inflation). To accumulate that amount by then, she will have to save almost $300 a month and invest it at an 8 percent a rate of return; at a 5 percent rate of return, she would have to save $675 a month.[6]

For most people, putting aside that much money every month is not easily done, and it is not very cost-effective. And there is another problem — if a person adopts this savings plan but needs long-term care before age 85, the funds accumulated by that time will fall short of her expenses. Clearly, for most people relying on savings and assets to pay for long-term care is not a feasible option.

A few individuals do have sufficient financial assets to pay long-term care costs. However, even for them there is the question of whether they want to take the gamble of possibly having to pay an uncapped liability (that is, a loss that has no fixed limit). If the gamble is lost, they may have to spend very large amounts of money on care, money that otherwise could have been used to enhance their quality of life or provide for their heirs.

Write down what you would say to help someone understand the drawbacks of planning to pay for long-term care with personal savings and assets.

Thinking

_____

_____

_____

_____

_____

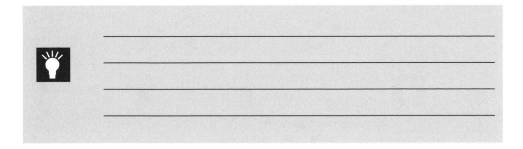

» Family Assistance

Traditionally, many people have relied on family members to provide long-term care. While such care is still very important, smaller families, a greater geographic dispersal of families, and more women holding jobs outside the home are shrinking the pool of potential family caregivers. High divorce rates also limit family caregiving. A recent study found that divorced parents are less likely to receive long-term care from their adult children than widowed elders. Single, elderly fathers who have been divorced are least likely to get help from their children. Even remarriage can make aging in place more difficult. About 30 percent of older people who have only stepchildren receive help with daily activities from a child, in contrast to 68 percent of those with biological children.[7]

A few people, while not expecting relatives to actually care for them, expect them to help pay for their care. This expectation, too, may not be realistic. The high cost of long-term care would put a strain on most family budgets. And adult children may find themselves caught between the desire to contribute to their parent's long-term care and their substantial financial obligations to fund their children's education and their own retirement. Finally, in many cases costs are simply greater than most families can afford, even with great sacrifice.

Thinking

Write down what you would say to help someone understand the implications of expecting to have long-term care provided or paid for by family members.

_____

_____

_____

_____

_____

_____

» Medicare

Medicare is a federal program that pays for health care for the elderly and a few other people. Many people (over half of Americans 45 and older) believe that Medicare covers extended nursing home stays for age-related or other chronic conditions.[8] This is not true. The Medicare program focuses on medical care, such as physician visits and hospital stays. Only certain long-term care services are covered and only in very limited circumstances. These services include skilled care related to recovery from an illness or rehabilitation for an injury. Medicare does not pay for ongoing personal or supervisory care, which represents the vast majority of long-term care needs. (In 2002, for example, Medicare benefits paid for only 17 percent of all long-term care expenditures.[9])

Specifically, Medicare covers skilled nursing and rehabilitation care in a nursing home only after a hospital stay of at least three days and only as required for recovery from an acute illness or injury. And although in theory benefits may be paid for up to 100 days, in practice few people continue to meet the requirements for benefits for more than a few weeks. Moreover, while Medicare pays the full cost of a patient's care for the first 20 days of an approved stay, for any additional days the patient must make a substantial daily copayment ($114 in 2005). And after a maximum of 100 days of nursing home care for each illness, Medicare pays nothing and the patient must bear all costs.

Medicare home health care benefits are also medically oriented, covering skilled nursing care and rehabilitative therapy at home as needed for recovery from an illness of injury. They do not cover the type of long-term care that most people need—personal assistance or homemaker services to help them age in place.

» Private Medicare Supplement Insurance

Even in the area Medicare focuses on, medical expenses, there are gaps in the benefits provided. Some medical services are not covered and must be paid for out of pocket. And for the services that are covered, beneficiaries must usually pay deductibles, copayments, and coinsurance. Consequently, a Medicare beneficiary with a serious illness or injury can incur large medical expenses that he must pay himself.

To address this situation, private insurance companies have developed **Medicare supplement policies**, sometimes referred to as **MedSupp policies** or **Medigap policies** (because they are designed to cover the gaps in Medicare). More recently, private insurers have offered Medicare health care management plans and Medicare private fee-for-service plans that serve the same purpose. Such plans are designed to enhance the hospital and physician care coverage of Medicare, but they do not extend coverage in the area of long-term care. For the small number of nursing home stays that qualify for Medicare coverage, a Medigap policy may cover the daily copayment. But the policy will not pay benefits for a nursing home stay not covered by Medicare, and it will not pay any benefits after Medicare's 100-day maximum has been reached.

In short, Medigap plans provide additional coverage for physician visits and hospital care, but they are not intended to meet long-term care needs, and they provide no coverage for the vast majority of long-term care expenses.

» Private Health Insurance and Disability Income Insurance

Many Americans under 65 are covered by private health insurance, most commonly through an employer-sponsored group plan. Some people expect to rely on this coverage to pay long-term care costs. They are mistaken.

This is because, like Medicare, most forms of health insurance focus on medical expenses such as hospital stays and physician visits, not the ongoing personal care and nonmedical services associated with long-term care. When private health insurance policies provide any coverage for long-term care services, they typically impose the same sort of limits as Medicare — that is, they cover only short-term skilled or recuperative care; they often require a prior hospital stay; and they pay only for a short period of care. They do not cover unskilled personal care or care for an extended time.

Many people also have disability income (DI) insurance. This coverage pays benefits when an insured suffers a disabling illness or injury. However, DI benefits are intended to replace some of the income a working-age person loses because of her inability to work. They do not cover the costs of either medical care or long-term care. Also, most DI policies do not provide benefits beyond age 65, further limiting their relevance to long-term care needs. However, many people are not aware of these limitations — in a recent "Long-Term Care IQ Test," nearly 20 percent of Americans ages 40 to 70 said that disability insurance pays for long-term care.[10]

» Medicaid

Medicaid is a federal-state program designed to meet the health care needs of the poor of all ages. Medicaid does pay benefits for nursing home care and, to a lesser extent, for some other long-term care services, but only on behalf of the impoverished and those who become impoverished paying for care.

A few people qualify for Medicaid when they first need long-term care because they have very limited income and assets. Others are not poor initially, but they **"spend down"** their assets — that is, they use up their own financial resources paying for long-term care until they have almost nothing left and qualify for Medicaid. (And of course, some people never qualify for Medicaid even though they have significant long-term care costs.)

To qualify for Medicaid, an individual may have assets of no more than about $2,000. When only one member of a married couple requires nursing home care, the asset limit is higher so that the spouse staying at home does not have to impoverish herself for the other spouse to qualify.

Because long-term care is so costly and many people do not plan ahead to cover these costs, Medicaid has become a major source of long-term care funding. In 2002 Medicaid spending accounted for nearly 47 percent of all long-term care expenditures.[11]

In addition to becoming impoverished, those who rely on Medicaid also pay a price in terms of the type of long-term care services available to them. Most state Medicaid programs provide few benefits for care outside a nursing home—specifically, in most states benefits for care at home are limited, and few programs cover assisted living. And Medicaid recipients may also have limited options in the facilities they can enter. Since in most states Medicaid reimbursement rates are generally lower than the rates paid by private patients, some nursing homes do not accept Medicaid recipients at all, and some give priority to private-pay patients.

Write down what you would say to help someone understand the implications of expecting to have long-term care paid for by Medicare, private Medicare supplement insurance, private health insurance, or Medicaid.

_____

_____

_____

_____

_____

Thinking

_____

_____

_____

_____

_____

_____

» Long-Term Care Insurance

In this chapter, we have seen that long-term care is expensive now and will be even more costly in the future. We have discussed how very few individuals can depend on their savings and assets to adequately pay for their long-term care needs. We have also seen that, in many instances, family members cannot provide the needed care or financial assistance. We have learned that Medicare benefits, Medicare supplement insurance, and private health insurance are extremely limited when it comes to long-term care and that relying on the Medicaid program has serious drawbacks.

For many people, a better approach than any of these is to privately purchase **long-term care insurance (LTCI)**. In this arrangement, an individual pays an insurance company regular premiums, and in return, when the individual needs long-term care services, the insurer pays benefits to help cover the cost of those services. Long-term care insurance has the following advantages:

■ **It provides benefits when they are needed to help pay long-term care expenses.** Planning to use savings or money from relatives to pay for care can be risky, because of the uncertainty of having sufficient funds when care is needed. A person expecting to be cared for by family members may find that they are not available when needed or are not qualified to provide the kind of care required. Medicare, Medicare supplement insurance, and private health insurance all fall far short of meeting long-term care needs. In contrast to all of these, a comprehensive LTCI policy ensures that benefits are provided when care is needed.

■ **It helps preserve savings and assets.** A person relying on his own funds or the very limited benefits of Medicare, Medicare supplements, or health insurance could see his assets wiped out by an extended period of long-term care. His plans for passing money on to his heirs, paying for the education of his grandchildren, or providing for his own or his spouse's quality of life in old age would be destroyed. And a person applying for Medicaid benefits has to spend almost all his assets as a condition of receiving those benefits. On the other hand, the holder of an LTCI policy will be able to rely on benefit payments to help cover care and can retain much more of his assets.

■ **It provides a greater range of care options.** Medicare does not pay for personal care for an extended period and generally does not pay for personal care at home unless skilled care is also needed. Medicaid recipients are not accepted by all nursing homes, and Medicaid seldom pays for care at home or in an assisted living residence. Those relying on their own savings and investments may find their choices limited by cost. But private LTCI policies can provide benefits for a wide array of services, so that the insured can choose the services that best meet his needs and allow him to age in place and retain his independence.

■ **It can enhance the quality of care.** Medicaid beneficiaries must often use facilities not in demand by others. And with the other options, limited funds may force an individual to choose care providers she would not otherwise select. With long-term care insurance, the money will be there to help pay for the facilities and services that the insured prefers.

Write down what you would say to help someone understand the advantages of long-term care insurance over other options for meeting the cost of long-term care.

_____

_____

_____

_____

Thinking

_____

_____

_____

_____

_____

_____

_____

» What's Next

In the next chapter, we will examine in more detail some of the ways that personal savings and assets can be used to meet the costs of long-term care. We will look at life insurance policies, home equity, and annuities as funding methods.

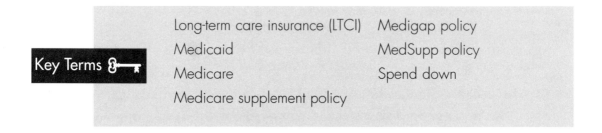

Key Terms

Long-term care insurance (LTCI)   Medigap policy
Medicaid   MedSupp policy
Medicare   Spend down
Medicare supplement policy

» Review Questions

1. What is the average daily cost of a semiprivate room in a nursing home? A private room?

2. What is the average hourly cost of a home health aide?

3. What are the seven funding sources that people may expect to draw on to pay for long-term care?

4. What are the limitations of using savings and assets to cover the cost of long-term care?

5. What are the limitations of relying on family members to provide or pay for long-term care?

6. What are the limitations of using Medicare to cover the cost of long-term care?

7. What are the limitations of using Medicare supplement insurance to cover the costs of long-term care?

8. What are the limitations of using private health insurance or disability income insurance to cover the costs of long-term care?

9. What are the limitations of using Medicaid to cover the costs of long-term care?

10. Compared to the other options, what are the benefits of using long-term care insurance to cover the costs of long-term care?

» Answers

1. $169; $192.

2. $18.

3. Personal savings and other financial assets, help from family members, the Medicare program, private Medicare supplement insurance, private health insurance and disability income insurance, the Medicaid program, and long-term care insurance.

4. For most people, putting aside sufficient funds to cover future long-term care costs is not easily done, and it is not very cost-effective. And if a person needs long-term care sooner than expected, the funds accumulated will fall short of expenses. Even those few with sufficient financial assets to cover long-term care costs run the risk of having to pay an uncapped liability and spending very large amounts on care.

5. Because of changes in society and family structure, a person expecting to be cared for by family members may find that they are not available when needed. In other cases, family members are available but are not qualified to provide the kind of care required. Expecting relatives to pay for care is often not realistic because of the high costs.

6. The Medicare program focuses on medical care, such as physician visits and hospital stays. Only certain long-term care services are covered and only in limited circumstances. Medicare does not pay for ongoing personal care, which represents the vast majority of long-term care needs.

7. Medicare supplement insurance is designed to enhance the hospital and physician care coverage of Medicare; it does not extend coverage in the area of long-term care.

8. Health insurance focuses on medical expenses such as hospital stays and physician visits, not the ongoing personal care and nonmedical services associated with long-term care. Disability income benefits are intended to replace some of the income a working-age person loses because of her inability to work, and they do not cover long-term care.

9. Unless a person is already poor, she must spend down her assets—that is, use up her own financial resources paying for long-term care until she has almost nothing left and qualifies for Medicaid. In addition to becoming impoverished, those who rely on Medicaid also pay a price in terms of the type of long-term care services available to them, as most state Medicaid programs provide few benefits for care outside a nursing home. Medicaid recipients may also have limited options in the facilities they can enter—since Medicaid reimbursement rates are generally lower than the rates paid by private patients, some nursing homes do not accept Medicaid recipients at all, and some give priority to private-pay patients.

10. A comprehensive LTCI policy ensures that benefits are provided when care is needed. It helps preserve savings and assets. It can provide benefits for a wide array of services, so that the insured can choose the services that best meet his needs and allow him to age in place and retain his independence. It can enhance the quality of care by ensuring that the money will be there to help pay for the facilities and services that the insured prefers.

NOTES

1 Mature Market Institute. September 2004. *The MetLife Market Survey of Nursing Home and Home Care Costs.*

2 Jones, A., National Center for Health Statistics. 2002. "The National Nursing Home Survey: 1999 Summary." *Vital Health Stat* 13(152).

3 Mature Market Institute. September 2004. *The MetLife Market Survey of Nursing Home and Home Care Costs.*

4 U.S. Department of Labor, Bureau of Labor Statistics. 2004.

5 Stucki, B. R., and Mulvey, J. 2000. *Can Baby Boomers Avoid the Nursing Home? Long-Term Care Insurance for "Aging in Place,"* p. 15. (Prepared for the American Council of Life Insurance.)

6 Savings calculations based on the self-funding tool on the web site of the Federal Long-Term Care Program, *www.ltcfeds.com/NASApp/ltc/do/assessing_your_needs/selffunding*.

7 Shone, B. S., and Pezzin, L. E. 1999. "Parental Marital Disruption and Intergenerational Transfers: An Analysis of Lone Elderly Parents and Their Children." *Demography* 36(3):287-297.

8 AARP. December 2001. "The Costs of Long-Term Care: Public Perceptions Versus Reality."

9 Georgetown University Long-Term Care Financing Project. July 2004. Fact sheet: "Who Pays for Long-Term Care?"

10 Mature Market Institute. October 2004. "The MetLife Long-Term Care IQ Test. Findings from a National Survey."

11 Georgetown University Long-Term Care Financing Project. July 2004. Fact sheet: "Medicaid and an Aging Population."

3

Personal Funding Sources

» What You Will Gain from This Chapter

As a result of the reading, research, and thinking you do in this chapter, you will be able to describe several personal funding sources for long-term care and explain their potential and limitations.

» Personal Funding Sources for Long-Term Care

The Centers for Medicare and Medicaid Services (CMS) estimated total spending on long-term care to be $180 billion in 2002. Of that, payments by private individuals from their own funds amounted to $37.2 billion, or 21 percent.[1]

There are four main sources of personal funds for meeting long-term care expenses:

- personal savings and assets,
- life insurance policies,
- home equity, and
- annuities.

Private savings and assets were discussed in the preceding chapter. In this chapter, we will look at the other sources, beginning with life insurance.

» Life Insurance

Funds can be obtained from a life insurance policy by means of accelerated death benefits, viatical settlements, and life settlements.

Accelerated Death Benefits

The **death benefit** of a life insurance policy is the payment the insurer makes if the insured dies. **Accelerated death benefits** (also known as **living benefits**) are payments of a portion or all of the death benefit before the death of the insured.

There are different types of accelerated death benefits for different purposes. For example, a catastrophic illness accelerated death benefit is paid when the insured is diagnosed with one of several specified medical conditions that require extensive or extraordinary treatment. The insured receiving this type of accelerated death benefit must use the money to pay for medical expenses not covered by his health insurance. A long-term care accelerated death benefit is paid when the insured needs long-term care, and the money must be used to pay for that care.

For an insurer to pay accelerated death benefits, an event specified in the policy (a **benefit trigger**) must occur. In early versions of these benefits, the insurer paid only if the insured suffered from a terminal illness, and that is still a common triggering event. However, most policies now allow for payment under other circumstances, and benefit triggers typically include one or more or the following:

- diagnosis of a terminal illness or physical condition, as a result of which death is likely to occur within a specified number of months;
- diagnosis of one of several specified critical illnesses;
- permanent confinement to a nursing home;
- the need for extended long-term care (in a facility, at home, or in the community) because of an inability to perform a specified number of ADLs; and
- a cognitive impairment.

Insurers must charge for the loss they incur by paying the death benefit early instead of keeping the money and earning investment income on it until the insured dies. An insurer may require a slightly higher premium, reduce the benefit amount, or treat the advance payment as a loan and charge interest.

The amount that an insured may obtain as an accelerated death benefit varies according to the policy. Many policies will pay up to a certain limit, defined either as a dollar figure or a percentage of the death benefit (usually at least 50 percent). Other policies will pay the full death benefit. A long-term care accelerated death benefit is often paid in monthly installments, with each payment equaling a percentage of the death benefit (generally between 2 and 5 percent). Money received as accelerated benefits by terminally or chronically ill individuals is not subject to income taxation.

An obvious drawback of using the accelerated death benefit of a life insurance policy to cover long-term care costs is that this defeats the primary purpose of life insurance. The money advanced is subtracted from the death benefit of the policy and so will not be available to pay estate taxes or a mortgage balance, or to provide income to the insured's family.

Another problem is that accelerated death benefits are not usually adequate to pay for long-term care for an extended period. The average person's life insurance policy has a death benefit of less than $100,000. An accelerated benefit of half that amount will not cover costs for the years that a person often needs care.

Research

If you have a life insurance policy, answer these questions about your policy:

■ Does it have an accelerated death benefits provision?
■ What are the triggers for the accelerated benefits?
■ What is the maximum that can be paid in accelerated benefits?
■ How is the insured charged for the accelerated benefit?

After you have done your reading and research, write down what you would say to help someone understand the potential and limitations of accelerated death benefits as a way to pay for long-term care.

Thinking

_____

_____

_____

_____

_____

_____

_____

_____

_____

Viatical Settlements

Viatical settlements take their name from the Latin word *viaticum*, meaning traveling provisions. In a viatical settlement, a terminally ill person sells his life insurance policy to a third party (that is, a party that is neither the insured nor the insurer). The proceeds from the sale of the policy then provide "monetary supplies" for the person's final journey to death.

Here is how a viatical settlement works: The third party, a **viatical company**, pays the terminally ill person, the **viator**, an amount of money. The amount is somewhat less than the death benefit of the viator's life insurance policy. In exchange, the viatical company becomes the owner and beneficiary of the policy. The viatical company also takes over payment of premiums on the policy. As a result of this transaction, the viator gets money while he is still alive, which he can use for any purpose, including paying for long-term care, and the viatical company receives the full death benefit after the viator dies.

From a viatical company's perspective, a person with a **terminal illness** is one who has a very short life expectancy — sometimes five years or less

TABLE 3.1

NAIC Guidelines for Viatical Payments

Life Expectancy	Percentage of Death Benefit Paid
1–6 months	80%
6–12 months	70%
12–18 months	65%
18–24 months	60%
Over 24 months	50%

but more typically two to three years or less. Individuals with chronic illnesses are also sometimes able to obtain viatical settlements.

The amount of payment is based on a percentage of the death benefit of the policy, and this percentage depends on the life expectancy of the viator. All other things being equal, the longer the life expectancy, the lower the percentage of the death benefit that the viatical company will pay. All reputable viatical companies offer payments based on the National Association of Insurance Commissioners (NAIC) guidelines. (See Table 3.1.)

Other factors affect the amount paid for a policy. These include:

■ **The rating of the insurer.** A viatical company will make a lower payment if the viator's life insurance company has an A. M. Best rating of B+ or lower. This is because the viatical company's risk is greater with lower-rated companies. These companies are more likely to go out of business than higher-rated insurers, and if they do, the viatical company will own a policy on which it may not be able to collect.

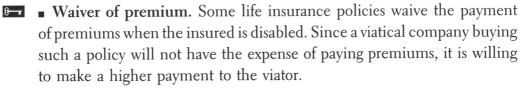 ■ **Waiver of premium.** Some life insurance policies waive the payment of premiums when the insured is disabled. Since a viatical company buying such a policy will not have the expense of paying premiums, it is willing to make a higher payment to the viator.

Under the Health Insurance Portability and Accountability Act of 1996 (HIPAA), the money a viator receives from a viatical settlement is tax-free, provided she has a life expectancy of two years or less, and provided the viatical company is licensed in the states in which it does business. The determination of life expectancy is made by a **licensed health care practitioner** (a physician or nurse), not the Internal Revenue Service. And if the viator does in fact live beyond two years, the IRS will not seek back taxes. A viatical payment made to a chronically ill person may also be tax-free, provided certain conditions are met.

As with accelerated death benefits, a viatical settlement defeats the purpose of life insurance, since when the insured dies no death benefit is available for taxes, mortgage payments, or survivors. However, for a dying person in need of long-term care services and without other means of paying for them, a viatical settlement may be an appropriate funding source.

Research

You can explore viaticals at several web sites: The National Association of Insurance Commissioners (*www.naic.org*), the Securities and Exchange Commission (*www.sec.gov*), the Federal Trade Commission (*www.ftc.gov/opa/1995/12/via.htm*), and the Viatical and Life Settlement Association of America (*www.viatical.org*).

Life Settlements

In many states today you hear of **life settlements** as well as viatical settlements. The two are similar in that both involve the sale of a life insurance policy to a third party. But for a life settlement, there is no requirement that the insured be terminally or chronically ill (although he must be elderly—generally only applicants over 70 are accepted).

As in a viatical settlement, in a life settlement an individual sells his policy to a company for a percentage of the death benefit. The company becomes the owner of the policy, pays the premiums, and receives the death benefit when the individual dies. The amount received is much lower than for a viatical settlement, since the life expectancy of the insured is much longer. The money can be used for any purpose, including paying for long-term care services or LTCI premiums.

Life settlements have their drawbacks. Unlike viatical payments, proceeds from a life settlement in excess of the total amount paid in premiums over the life of the policy may be taxable. And as with a viatical settlement, the insured's beneficiaries will receive no death benefit. But if the death benefit is not really needed (as might be the case if a person's spouse has died and his children have become self-supporting), or if the premiums have become unaffordable, obtaining a life settlement may be a reasonable course of action.

After you have done your reading and research, write down what you would say to help someone understand both the potential and the limitations of viatical settlements and life settlements as a way to pay for long-term care.

Thinking

_____

_____

_____

_____

_____

_____

_____

_____

_____

» Home Equity and Reverse Mortgages

The principal financial asset of many older people is **home equity**, that is, the value of the home they own after any mortgage amount owed or other liability has been subtracted. The amount of home equity can be substantial, especially if the home was purchased years ago and the mortgage has been largely or wholly paid off. In such cases, home equity can be an important source of funds to cover long-term care costs.

In the past, there were only two ways of turning home equity into funds that could be used to pay for long-term care—selling the home or taking out a home equity loan. Each of these alternatives has serious drawbacks. Selling can mean leaving a longtime residence, and payments must be made on a home equity loan. Fortunately, there are now several new methods of drawing on home equity. Here we will discuss the most popular—reverse mortgages.

A **reverse mortgage** is a type of home equity loan. We can best understand how it works by comparing it to regular mortgages and conventional home equity loans.

- In a **regular mortgage**, a bank or other lending institution lends a person the money she needs to buy a home, and the person pays the lender back with interest by means of monthly payments. The home is security for the loan.

- In a conventional **home equity loan,** a bank lends money to someone who already owns a home outright or has substantial equity in one, with the home or the equity serving as security for the loan. As with a mortgage, in a conventional home equity loan the borrower must make regular payments to the lender.

- In a reverse mortgage, as in a conventional home equity loan, a bank lends money to a homeowner with the home serving as security. However, in a reverse mortgage the homeowner does not have to make regular payments to the lender. Instead, the loan (plus accumulated interest) must be paid off only when the homeowner dies, sells the home, or moves out of the home.

The advantage of a reverse mortgage for an elderly person is clear—the person can obtain funds from his home equity without having to worry about being able to make loan payments as in a conventional home equity loan.

The lender's payment to the homeowner can be made in one of four ways: in a lump sum, in monthly payments, through a line of credit to be drawn on as needed, or by a combination of these. The fact that in most cases the lender makes regular or periodic payments to the homeowner (instead of the homeowner making regular payments to the lender as in a regular mortgage) is why this arrangement is called a reverse mortgage.

The lender's payment to the homeowner is not subject to income tax, since it is not income but a loan that will eventually be repaid. Interest on a reverse mortgage is not tax-deductible until it is actually paid—that is, at the end of the loan period when the debt is paid off.

A homeowner taking out a reverse mortgage retains title to her home and is responsible for maintaining the home and paying real estate taxes. If the homeowner dies, the lender does not take title to the home, but the homeowner's heirs must pay off the loan. Usually the debt is repaid by selling the home or refinancing the property with a traditional mortgage.

There are different types of reverse mortgages, and whether a person qualifies for one depends on the type she is applying for. But generally speaking, a homeowner must be at least 62 years old, and the home must be her principal residence. The amount a lender advances a homeowner depends on several factors, including the value of the home, the homeowner's age, the interest rate charged, the type of reverse mortgage, the payout method selected by the homeowner, and, for federally insured reverse mortgages, local lending limits established by the Federal Housing Administration (FHA).

A reverse mortgage is an effective way for a homeowner to tap into home equity without selling her home and moving, and the money obtained can be used to pay for long-term care or long-term care insurance. However, this money can be used only for home care, since if the borrower leaves her home to enter an assisted living residence or a nursing home the mortgage must be paid off. Additionally, a person taking out a reverse mortgage will substantially reduce her home equity, leaving her with less to rely on as a financial reserve and to pass on to her heirs. Finally, the funds obtained from a reverse mortgage may not be adequate to pay a person's long-term care costs.

Research

The AARP web site has a good piece, "Reverse Mortgages," starting at *www.aarp.org/revmort*. There is also an article on the web site of the U.S. Department of Housing and Urban Development (HUD). Go to *www.hud.gov/offices/hsg/sfh/hecm/rmtopten.cfm.*

Thinking

After you have done your reading and research, write down what you would say to help someone understand the potential and limitations of a reverse mortgage as a way to pay for long-term care.

_____

_____

_____

_____

_____

_____

_____

_____

_____

_____

» Annuities

An **annuity** is a type of investment. The investor (called the **annuitant**) pays money to an insurance company or financial institution, and in return the insurer makes regular payments to the annuitant over a period of time. Depending on the type of annuity, this period may be for as long as the annuitant lives or for a limited, predetermined time. The amount of the payments made to the annuitant may be fixed and unchanging, or it may vary according to the investment performance of the money the annuitant paid.

The payments from an annuity can be used to pay the cost of long-term care services. Alternatively, an annuity can be used in combination with long-term care insurance. The annuity income pays for the premiums of an LTCI policy, and the policy covers the costs of care. Let us examine how this works.

Premiums for long-term care insurance can range from $500 to over $5,000 a year, depending on how the policy is structured. How can an individual wanting to include long-term care insurance in her retirement plans ensure that, given all her other financial needs, she will have up to $5,000 or more to pay her LTCI policy premiums every year as long as she lives?

One answer is to set aside a fund of money in a safe, interest-bearing investment and pay long-term care premiums from the interest this fund generates. But this approach has a number of disadvantages:

■ Such a fund ties up a huge amount of money. If banks are paying 4 percent interest annually, it will take $125,000 to generate the needed $5,000 each year.

■ If interest rates fall, the amount generated by the fund will decrease, and other funds will have to be used to help pay the premiums.

■ As long as a fund is generating income, it is also generating income tax liability. In the 15 percent tax bracket, the federal income tax liability on $5,000 in interest earnings is $750. In the 28 percent bracket, it is $1,400.

Another alternative would be to purchase a **single-premium fixed life annuity**. In this type of annuity, the annuitant makes a one-time payment (the single premium) to an insurer, and in return the insurer pays the annuitant a fixed amount of money every year for as long as he lives. A person age 60 might be able to purchase an annuity that would pay $5,000 annually for life for about $85,000, $40,000 less than the amount needed to generate that much through an interest-bearing investment. At age 65, a $5,000 annuity could be purchased for about $67,000. (The older the purchaser, the fewer years the financial institution will likely have to pay the annuity, so the less it charges.) And the annuity payments would be partially tax-free.

In order to offer a simple example, we have described above a pure life annuity. However, most people choose an annuity that guarantees that at least the amount of money paid in will be paid out—in other words, if the annuitant dies before he has received payments totaling the amount he paid for the annuity, payments will be made to his beneficiaries until that amount is reached. Of course, such an annuity costs more or makes lower payments than a pure life annuity.

A fixed annuity such as the one described above is guaranteed to pay the agreed-upon amount, nothing less. There are also variable annuities, in which the payment amount varies with the performance of the investments the annuity funds are placed in. With such an annuity, there is no guarantee that the payment amount will be sufficient to cover long-term care expenses or LTCI premiums, so it may not be a suitable approach for someone seeking to provide for these costs.

Finally, note another combination of funding sources: Some people use funds from a reverse mortgage to buy an annuity and then use the annuity income to pay for long-term care or LTCI premiums.

Annuities are discussed in more detail in Chapter 11.

Thinking

After you have done your reading, write down what you would say to help someone understand the potential and limitations of an annuity as a way to pay for long-term care.

_____

_____

_____

_____

_____

_____

_____

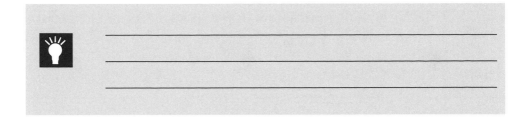

» What's Next

In the next chapter, we will look at the Medicare program. We will learn what benefits it provides and why it does not meet long-term care needs.

Key Terms 🗝

Accelerated death benefits	Living benefits
Annuitant	Regular mortgage
Annuity	Reverse mortgage
Benefit trigger	Single-premium fixed life
Death benefit	annuity
Home equity	Terminal illness
Home equity loan	Viatical company
Licensed health care	Viatical settlement
practitioner	Viator
Life settlement	Waiver of premium

» Review Questions

1. What are accelerated death benefits?

2. What are the three ways in which insurers can charge for the cost of accelerated death benefits?

3. What is the tax status of accelerated death benefits?

4. What are the drawbacks of using the accelerated death benefits of a life insurance policy to cover long-term care costs?

5. How does a viatical settlement work?

6. What factors affect the amount paid in a viatical settlement?

7. What is the tax status of money received from a viatical settlement?

8. How do viatical settlements and life settlements differ?

9. How does a reverse mortgage compare to a conventional home equity loan?

10. What are the advantages of using a fixed life annuity to pay LTCI premiums?

» Answers

1. The payment of all or a portion of the death benefit of a life insurance policy before the death of the insured. Payment is made when a benefit trigger specified in the policy, such as diagnosis with a terminal or critical illness or the need for long-term care, occurs.

2. They can require a slightly higher premium, reduce the benefit amount, or treat the advance payment as a loan and charge interest.

3. Accelerated benefits paid to terminally or chronically ill insureds are not subject to federal income taxes.

4. The money advanced is subtracted from the death benefit of the policy and will not be available to beneficiaries; accelerated death benefits are not usually adequate to pay for long-term care for an extended period.

5. A viatical company pays a terminally ill person an amount of money, and in exchange the company becomes the owner and beneficiary of his life insurance policy. The terminally ill person gets money while he is still alive, and the viatical company receives the full death benefit after he dies.

6. The amount of payment is based on a percentage of the death benefit of the policy, which depends on the life expectancy of the viator. Other factors include the rating of the insurer and whether the policy waives premiums when the insured is disabled.

7. The money a viator receives from a viatical settlement is tax-free, provided she has a life expectancy of two years or less, and provided the viatical company is licensed in the states in which it does business. A viatical payment made to a chronically ill person may also be tax-free, provided certain conditions are met.

8. For a life settlement, there is no requirement that the insured be terminally or chronically ill. Also, unlike viatical payments, proceeds from a life settlement in excess of the total amount paid in premiums over the life of the policy may be taxable.

9. In a reverse mortgage, as in a conventional home equity loan, a bank lends money to a homeowner with the home serving as security. However, in a reverse mortgage the homeowner does not have to make regular payments to the lender. Instead, the loan (plus accumulated interest) must be paid off only when the homeowner dies, sells the home, or moves out of the home.

10. A fixed life annuity is guaranteed to pay the agreed-upon amount, nothing less, for the life of the annuitant. And the annuity payments are partially tax-free during the life expectancy of the annuitant.

NOTE

1 Centers for Medicare and Medicaid Services, Office of the Actuary, National Health Statistics Group. 2004. Unpublished.

The Medicare Program

4

» What You Will Gain from This Chapter

As a result of the reading, research, and thinking you do in this chapter, you will be able to describe the Medicare program and explain why it does not meet the needs of those requiring long-term care.

» What Is Medicare?

Medicare is a federal health care benefits program. It helps pay for medical services (such as hospital stays and physician visits) of people age 65 and older, as well as some persons under 65 who are disabled or suffer permanent kidney failure (end-stage renal disease).

A Medicare beneficiary may choose the original Medicare plan or (where available) a Medicare Advantage plan. The original Medicare plan operates on a fee-for-service basis. Medicare reimburses health care providers who serve beneficiaries by paying them a fee for each service rendered. Beneficiaries can go to any physician, hospital, or other provider that accepts Medicare fees as payment. Beneficiaries must pay a deductible, and they also usually pay a portion of the cost of covered services in the form of copayments and coinsurance. The original Medicare plan has two parts:

- **Medicare Part A** primarily covers inpatient care in hospitals.
- **Medicare Part B** primarily covers physician services, outpatient hospital care, and some other medical services not covered by Part A.

Medicare Advantage (formerly Medicare+Choice, also called Medicare Part C) is a program under which private-sector health insurance plans provide coverage to Medicare beneficiaries. It consists of health care management plans, such as health maintenance organizations (HMOs) and preferred provider organizations (PPOs), as well as private fee-for-service plans.

The Medicare Prescription Drug, Improvement, and Modernization Act of 2003 (commonly called simply the Medicare Modernization Act, or MMA) will create Medicare Part D, a new prescription drug benefit program that will begin operating in January 2006.

Go to the Medicare web site, *www.medicare.gov*. From the menu on the left, select and read "Plan Choices." After you have read about the original Medicare plan and Medicare Advantage, explore the rest of the site. Or call Medicare at 1-800-MEDICARE for information.

» Eligibility for Medicare

Those at least 65 years old and eligible for retirement benefits from Social Security or the Railroad Retirement system can enroll in Medicare Part A without paying a premium. Some persons 65 and over who are covered by government employee retirement plans instead of Social Security are also eligible for Part A at no charge. Those 65 and over who do not fall into one of these categories can enroll in Medicare Part A, but they must pay a premium. Medicare Part A coverage is also extended to persons of any age who are disabled or suffer permanent kidney failure (end-stage renal disease) and meet certain criteria.

Anyone 65 or over can enroll in Medicare Part B, as can disabled persons eligible for Medicare Part A, but all must pay a monthly premium ($78.20 in 2005, rising to $89.20 in 2006).

Go to the Medicare web site, *www.medicare.gov*. Search for the "Medicare Eligibility Tool," then click on the "General Enrollment and Eligibility" tab at the top to read general information about Medicare.

After you have done your reading and research, write down what you would say to help someone understand who is eligible for Medicare.

Thinking

_____

_____

_____

_____

_____

_____

_____

_____

_____

_____

_____

» Medicare and Long-Term Care

The Medicare program was created to help pay the medical expenses of the elderly, and it primarily covers hospital and physician services. Medicare does provide very limited benefits under limited circumstances in two areas associated with long-term care—nursing home care and home health care. But as we will see, these benefits do not meet the need for ongoing personal care or supervisory care, which is the focus of long-term care.

Nursing Home Coverage

A Medicare beneficiary can receive benefits for care in a skilled nursing facility provided all of the following conditions are met:

■ The individual needs skilled care. The individual may require personal or supervisory care in support of skilled care, but if he needs *only* personal or supervisory care, he is not eligible for benefits.

■ A physician has determined that there is a **medical necessity** for skilled care—this means that skilled care is required for the diagnosis and treatment of a medical condition. In practice, benefits are paid to those who need care to help them recuperate from an acute illness or injury and regain normal functioning. Benefits are not paid to those who need care indefinitely to help them cope with a chronic impairment.

■ The individual has had an inpatient hospital stay of at least three consecutive days within the last 30 days.

■ The skilled nursing facility is certified by Medicare. (Most are, but not all.)

In theory, Medicare can pay up to 100 days of nursing home benefits per benefit period. But in practice this does not often happen, as few people continue to meet the medical necessity requirement for very long. Most people recover from their injury or illness within a few weeks, so that care is no longer medically necessary. Others do not fully recover and become chronically impaired. These people also cease to meet the medical necessity requirement because they no longer need skilled care for the diagnosis and treatment of a medical condition, but instead need personal care to cope with their impairment.

In those cases in which Medicare continues to pay benefits beyond 20 days, the beneficiary must make a daily copayment of $114, as shown in Table 4.1.

In summary, although Medicare does provide some benefits for nursing home care, these benefits do not meet long-term care needs for the following reasons:

TABLE 4.1

Medicare Nursing Home Benefits and Cost-Sharing*

Time Period	Medicare Pays	Beneficiary Pays
Day 1–20	100%	Nothing
Day 21–100	Any costs in excess of $114 a day	$114 daily copayment
After day 100	Nothing	All costs

* Amounts for 2005, adjusted annually. Benefits are paid only provided the beneficiary continues to meet all the requirements described in the text, including medical necessity.

■ No benefits are paid if the beneficiary needs personal or supervisory care only, not skilled care.

■ No benefits are paid for skilled care unless it is medically necessary.

■ If benefits are provided, Medicare covers all expenses only for the first 20 days, after which the beneficiary pays $114 per day and Medicare pays any charges exceeding this amount.

■ No benefits are paid beyond 100 days.

Research

Go to the Medicare web site, *www.medicare.gov*. Click on "Find a Medicare Publication," type in the Publication ID number 10153, and read "Medicare and Skilled Nursing Facility Care." Also look at Publication ID 02223, "Choosing Long-Term Care" for good general information about long-term care and other resources in this area.

Thinking

After you have done your reading and research, write down what you would say to explain to someone the limitations of Medicare benefits for nursing home care.

_____

_____

_____

_____

_____

_____

_____

_____

_____

_____

_____

Home Health Care Coverage

To receive Medicare benefits for home health care, an individual must meet four conditions:

■ A physician certifies the medical necessity of intermittent (part-time) skilled nursing care or physical, speech, or occupational therapy. If the individual needs only personal or supervisory care, she is not eligible for benefits.

■ The physician certifies that the individual needs to receive care at home, and the physician develops a plan of care.

■ The individual is **homebound**—that is, she is unable to leave home without a major effort. When she does leave home, it must be infrequently and for a short time, and it must be for an urgent purpose, such as to get medical care or to attend religious services.

■ The home health care agency caring for the individual must be Medicare-certified. (Many agencies are, but not all.)

If all these conditions are met, Medicare pays for intermittent skilled nursing care and therapy. In some cases other services and supplies required to support skilled care, such as home health aide services or durable medical equipment, may also be covered. Medicare pays the full approved amount for covered services, except for 20 percent coinsurance for durable medical equipment.

There is no set limit to the duration and amount of home care benefits a person can receive. But like nursing home benefits, in practice home care benefits are seldom paid for very long because people seldom continue to meet the medical necessity requirement for very long.

In summary, Medicare does provide home health care benefits, but because personal or supervisory care is not covered unless skilled care is also needed, and because few people qualify for benefits and even fewer qualify for more than a short time, these benefits do not meet long-term care needs.

Research

Go to the Medicare web site, *www.medicare.gov*. Click on "Find a Medicare Publication," and select and read Publication ID number 10969, "Medicare and Home Health Care."

Thinking

After you have done your reading and research, write down what you would say to explain to someone the limitations of Medicare benefits for home health care.

_____

_____

_____

_____

_____

_____

_____

_____

_____

_____

_____

» Medicare Supplement Insurance and Medicare Advantage

Many Medicare beneficiaries buy **Medicare supplement (MedSupp) insurance**. This is private health insurance that fills some of the gaps of Medicare coverage (hence it is often called **Medigap insurance**). Specifically, Medigap policies pay some of the deductibles, copayments, and coinsurance amounts that beneficiaries must otherwise pay themselves, and some policies also offer a few additional benefits not provided by Medicare. Medigap policies may include two benefits for services associated with long-term care.

■ Some Medigap plans provide **at-home recovery benefits**. These help pay for personal care in the insured's home while he is recovering from an illness or injury and receiving Medicare benefits for skilled care at home. Benefits may also continue for a limited time after skilled care is no longer needed. But for two reasons these benefits contribute little to meeting the need for ongoing personal care. First, the insured must initially meet the stringent conditions for Medicare home health care benefits described in this chapter — in other words, skilled care must be medically necessary for the insured's recovery from an acute injury or illness. Second, benefits are limited to a total of eight weeks and $1,600 a year.

■ Most Medigap plans cover the daily copayment that Medicare charges after the 20th day of nursing home care. But this benefit also has a limited impact, since it too applies only to those who are recovering from an injury or illness and meet Medicare's medical necessity requirement. Moreover, since people seldom continue to meet this requirement much beyond 20 days, this benefit is not often paid for very long.

Clearly, neither of these benefits goes very far in meeting the needs of those requiring long-term care for an extended period.

Individuals enrolled in both Medicare Part A and Part B have the option of participating in a Medicare Advantage plan, a private health insurance plan that contracts with the Medicare program to provide benefits to Medicare beneficiaries. Medicare Advantage plans provide the normal Medicare benefits package, and (like Medigap policies) they also offer some additional benefits that fill some of the gaps of Medicare coverage. However, also like Medigap policies, Medicare Advantage plans do not provide any significant coverage in the area of long-term care.

» What's Next

In the next chapter, we will look at the Medicaid program. We will learn how it works and what potential and limitations it has for covering the costs of long-term care.

Key Terms 𝕆⸺⚷

At-home recovery benefits	Medicare Part A
Homebound	Medicare Part B
Medical necessity	Medicare supplement (MedSupp) insurance
Medicare	
Medicare Advantage	Medigap insurance

» Review Questions

1. What is the purpose of the Medicare program?

2. What does Medicare Part A primarily cover?

3. What does Medicare Part B primarily cover?

4. Who is eligible for Medicare Part B? Who must pay a premium for Part B?

5. Medicare pays nursing home benefits to those who need (personal care only / supervisory care only / skilled care).

6. What does it mean to say that skilled care is medically necessary?

7. What benefits does Medicare provide for nursing home care?

8. What benefits does Medicare provide for home health care?

9. What limits are there on Medicare home health care benefits?

10. Why does the at-home recovery benefit provided by some Medigap policies contribute little to meeting the need for long-term care?

» Answers

1. Medicare helps pay for medical services (such as hospital stays and physician visits) of people age 65 and older, as well as some persons under 65 who are disabled or suffer permanent kidney failure (end-stage renal disease).

2. Medicare Part A primarily covers inpatient care in hospitals.

3. Medicare Part B primarily covers physician services, outpatient hospital care, and some other medical services not covered by Part A.

4. Anyone 65 or over is eligible for Medicare Part B, as are disabled persons eligible for Medicare Part A. Everyone must pay a premium.

5. Skilled care.

6. It means that skilled care is required for the diagnosis and treatment of a medical condition.

7. If nursing home benefits are provided, Medicare pays all covered expenses for the first 20 days, after which the beneficiary pays $114 per day and Medicare pays any charges exceeding this amount. There is no coverage beyond 100 days.

8. Medicare pays for intermittent skilled nursing care and therapy. In some cases other services and supplies required to support skilled care, such as home health aide services or durable medical equipment, may also be covered. Medicare pays the full approved amount for covered services, except for 20 percent coinsurance for durable medical equipment.

9. There is no set limit to the duration and amount of home care benefits a person can receive. But as with nursing home benefits, in practice home care benefits are seldom paid for very long because people seldom continue to meet the medical necessity requirement for very long.

10. The insured must initially meet the stringent conditions for Medicare home health care benefits, including medical necessity. And benefits are limited to a total of eight weeks and $1,600 a year.

 5

The Medicaid Program

» What You Will Gain from This Chapter

As a result of the reading, research, and thinking you do in this chapter, you will be able to describe the Medicaid program and explain its potential and limitations in covering the costs of long-term care.

» What Is Medicaid?

Medicaid is a federal-state program that pays for health care services for poor people of all ages. The federal government establishes broad guidelines for the operation of Medicaid, but each state administers its own program and has some flexibility in determining eligibility criteria; the type, amount, and duration of services its program pays for; and rates of payment for services. Consequently, a person who is eligible for Medicaid in one state may not be eligible in another state, and the benefits provided in one state may differ considerably from the benefits provided in another state. Also, state Medicaid programs may change from year to year in response to changing needs or emerging problems. The reader is advised to learn about the specific eligibility requirements and benefit provisions that currently apply to his or her state's program.

Medicaid is jointly funded by the federal government and the state governments. In 2003 the federal government provided 50 to 77 percent of funds, depending on the state, with an average federal contribution of 61 percent.[1] The states paid the rest.

Go to the web site of the Centers for Medicare and Medicaid Services (CMS), *www.cms.gov*, select "Medicaid," and read the general information for consumers.

» Benefits

Medicaid's federal guidelines require all state Medicaid programs to provide a minimal benefit package, including hospital inpatient and outpatient care, physician care, and many other services. In the area of long-term care, all state programs must cover nursing home care, and they are also required to provide benefits for home health care for those who are **nursing home eligible** (those who would need nursing home care if they did not receive home care). And although it is not required, some states also pay benefits for home and community-based services (such as home health aides and adult day centers) for certain other Medicaid beneficiaries. But eligibility for these benefits may be restricted, and funding is limited—while there is considerable variation from state to state, nationally only about 23 percent of Medicaid long-term care spending goes to home and community-based services.[2] Finally, state Medicaid programs are not required to pay for care in an assisted living residence, and they generally do not.

In summary, Medicaid long-term care benefits are focused on nursing home care, with only limited benefits available for other settings and services. On the other hand, Medicaid is the only government program that provides substantial coverage of long-term care. Medicaid spending on long-term care was $84.7 billion in 2002, accounting for nearly 47 percent of all long-term care expenditures.[3]

It should also be noted that payment for services is made by state Medicaid programs directly to health care providers, not to Medicaid beneficiaries.

For information about the benefits provided by your state's Medicaid program, go to *www.cms.gov*, click on state programs, and select your state (or go directly to *www.cms.hhs.gov/medicaid/statemap.asp*).

» Eligibility

To be eligible for Medicaid, a person must be poor. This means that the value of her financial assets and her income must be below certain levels, called **eligibility limits**. However, many people who are not poor when they first need long-term care obtain Medicaid benefits by becoming poor. They **spend down**—that is, they use the assets they have accumulated over a lifetime to pay for long-term care until they have very little left, and they spend almost all their income on care. Then they meet Medicaid's eligibility limits and can receive benefits for Medicaid-covered services. This approach works, but it has disadvantages—some obvious, some not so obvious—as we will see.

Assets

The Medicaid asset eligibility limit varies from state to state, as the federal government allows some flexibility, but it is generally about $2,000 for a single person and $3,000 for a married couple when both spouses are applying for Medicaid. (When only one spouse is applying, spousal impoverishment rules come into play; these are discussed below.)

Medicaid divides financial assets into two categories: **countable assets** are those that are considered in determining whether a person exceeds the eligibility limit, and **noncountable assets** are those that are not. Countable assets include:

- cash;
- bank accounts, such as savings and checking accounts;
- stocks, bonds, annuities, and certificates of deposit (CDs);
- IRAs, Keogh accounts, and other retirement funds;
- trusts;
- the cash surrender value of life insurance policies (that is, the amount the individual can obtain by terminating the policies) with a combined face value greater than $1,500; and
- items that may be converted into cash, including vacation homes, second vehicles, and any other items not specifically listed as noncountable assets by Medicaid.

If the total value of a person's countable assets exceeds the eligibility limit, he is not eligible for Medicaid. To become eligible, he must spend all countable assets above the eligibility limit on care; illiquid assets, such as houses and vehicles, must be sold and the money spent on care.

Noncountable assets are not counted in calculating whether the eligibility limit has been exceeded, and they do not have to be sold to pay for care. They include:

- the applicant's home (his primary residence);
- household goods and personal effects such as furniture and clothing;
- one automobile;
- the cash surrender value of life insurance policies with a combined face value of less than $1,500; and
- a few minor items such as wedding rings and burial plots.

If a Medicaid beneficiary leaves his home to live in a long-term care facility, the home may in theory be considered countable and the beneficiary can be forced to sell it to pay for care. But in practice this rarely occurs because of numerous conditions and restrictions. However, in this situation some state Medicaid programs may place a lien against the property, and when the beneficiary or his spouse dies, the property is subject to **estate recovery** — that is, the Medicaid program collects from the estate the amount of the benefits it has provided. But not all states use Medicaid liens, and the states differ considerably in how they administer estate recovery and how estate recovery provisions interact with state probate laws, so that there is a great deal of variation in what assets states actually recover. For example, some states have homestead provisions that protect a primary residence from creditors (including Medicaid) and allow it to pass to heirs unencumbered.

After you have done your reading, write down what you would say to help someone understand countable and noncountable assets under Medicaid.

_____

_____

Income

Income eligibility limits, like assets limits, vary from state to state, but in all states they are very low. Most states' limits are below those of the Supplemental Security Income (SSI) program (in 2005, $579 per month for individuals, $869 for couples).[4] Some states grant Medicaid eligibility to certain persons with incomes above SSI levels, but only within limits — generally no higher than the federal poverty level (in 2005, $9,520 annually for an individual and $12,780 for a couple[5]) or, for those who qualify for special eligibility options, 300 percent of SSI levels.

In calculating whether a person's income exceeds the eligibility limit, Medicaid counts all but the first $20 per month of unearned income, such as Social Security benefits, other government and private pensions, veterans' benefits, workers' compensation, annuity payments, and investment income. Food stamps and certain other forms of public assistance and charity are not counted. (A portion of any earned income, such as wages or earnings from self-employment, is not counted, but this is of course not normally relevant to applicants in need of long-term care.)

If a person qualifies for Medicaid and enters a nursing home, almost all her income must be spent on care. She may retain only a small **personal needs allowance** (usually between $30 and $75 per month) to cover such items as beauty supplies and reading material. In addition, any income used to pay health insurance premiums may be retained.

For information about your state's eligibility requirements, go to *www.cms.gov*, click on state programs, and select your state (or go directly to *www.cms.hhs.gov/medicaid/statemap.asp*).

Spousal Impoverishment Rules

In the past, when one of the spouses of a married couple needed nursing home care and applied for Medicaid, to enable him to qualify the couple had to spend almost all their combined countable assets and income on his care. Meanwhile, the spouse who did not need care and still lived at home (referred to as the **community spouse**) was left with almost no income or assets. This situation came to be known as **spousal impoverishment** and was a serious problem. Some couples would even divorce so that the community spouse could retain enough income and assets to live on while the other spouse qualified for Medicaid.

To address this problem, changes were made in the Medicaid eligibility rules. Now, a community spouse who has her own sources of income does not have to spend that income on the care of a spouse in a nursing home. In addition, a community spouse with little or no income of her own is permitted a **minimum monthly maintenance needs allowance**. This means that if a community spouse's own monthly income is less than a floor amount, she can receive enough of the income of the nursing home spouse to make up the difference. In 2005 the monthly floor amounts used by state programs ranged from $1,561.25 to $2,377.50.[6]

A couple's countable assets are also divided between the community spouse and the nursing home spouse. All states must allow the community spouse to retain all countable assets up to a minimum amount set by the federal government ($19,020 in 2005). States have the option of also allowing the community spouse to keep half of assets in excess of the minimum up to a certain limit. This limit cannot be higher than a federal maximum

($95,100 in 2005), but it may be less than that maximum—for example, a state might let the community spouse retain the minimum of $19,020 plus half of assets up to $50,000.[7] All of the couple's countable assets in excess of the eligibility limit that are not allocated to the community spouse according to these rules must be spent on the nursing home spouse's care. (All noncountable assets are of course retained by the couple and are not required to be spent on care.)

Research   Go to the CMS web site, *www.cms.gov*, search "spousal Impoverishment," and read the information.

Thinking   After you have done your reading and research, write down what you would say to help someone understand how Medicaid treats the assets and income of applicants.

_____

_____

_____

_____

_____

_____

_____

_____

_____

_____

_____

_____

Transfers of Assets

It would seem that a simple way around Medicaid eligibility rules would be for the Medicaid applicant to give assets to family members or place them in a trust. In this way, the assets could be legally transferred to heirs and not spent to meet eligibility limits. While in the past this approach was advocated by some financial planners, rules enacted by Congress have placed significant limits on it.

Under these rules, a state Medicaid program must withhold payment of certain benefits to a Medicaid beneficiary who makes a **transfer of assets** in which he receives less than the value of the assets (as would occur if he gave them to someone or sold them to a family member for less than they were worth). There is a 36-month **look-back period**—that is, Medicaid withholds benefits if such a transaction has taken place 36 months or less before the application for Medicaid. For transfers to an irrevocable trust, the look-back period is 60 months.

If Medicaid finds that such a transfer has occurred, benefits are withheld for an amount of time referred to as the **penalty period**. The length of the penalty period for nursing home care is determined by dividing the value of the assets transferred by the state's **average monthly private-pay rate** for nursing home care. (The private-pay rate is that charged to those paying for care themselves or through private long-term care insurance.) For example: Thomas Manning transferred an asset worth $250,000 to his daughter six months before applying for Medicaid, without receiving anything in return. The $250,000 is divided by the average monthly private-pay rate for nursing homes in the state ($5,000), resulting in a 50-month penalty period. This means that Thomas cannot receive Medicaid benefits for over four years. There is no limit to the length of a penalty period.[8]

Because of this penalty, it is generally not in an individual's interest to transfer assets to family members. And in cases where such transfers are financially advantageous, they have a serious drawback—the individual loses legal control of his assets and must rely on others for his financial needs.

Research   Go to the CMS web site, *www.cms.gov*, search "transfer of assets," and read the information.

After you have done your reading and research, write down what you would say to help someone understand the Medicaid rules governing transfers of assets.

Thinking 💡

_____

_____

_____

_____

_____

_____

_____

_____

_____

_____

_____

» The Disadvantages of Relying on Medicaid

Spending down to qualify for Medicaid results in a loss of financial independence. An elderly person who has worked hard and been self-supporting her whole life becomes indigent and must depend on the government for her needs. Spending down also means that hard-earned assets cannot be used for such purposes as helping grandchildren go to college, and they cannot be left to heirs.

There is another important disadvantage to this approach to meeting long-term care needs—a Medicaid beneficiary may have a limited choice of long-term care facilities, and the most desirable facilities may not be available to her. Why is this? In most states, Medicaid pays facilities less for caring for Medicaid beneficiaries than they receive from private patients. This has a number of consequences:

■ Some nursing homes do not accept Medicaid beneficiaries. Typically these are facilities that have superior reputations and are in great demand, which means that all beds can be filled without taking lower-paying

Medicaid patients. A person who goes on Medicaid will not have the option of entering these facilities.

■ Most nursing homes that do accept Medicaid patients allocate only a limited number of beds to them. The most in-demand of these facilities have long waiting lists for Medicaid beds, so a Medicaid beneficiary may be forced to enter a less popular nursing home.

■ If an individual urgently needs nursing home care, she may have to go wherever a Medicaid bed is available. This may not be in a facility near her family and friends.

It is true that all facilities that care for Medicaid patients must be certified by Medicaid and meet certain standards. But among facilities meeting those standards there are differences, and Medicaid patients tend to find a place in those that others find less desirable.

Yet another drawback to relying on Medicaid is limited care options. As discussed previously, the Medicaid program is largely focused on nursing home care, with only limited benefits available for home and community-based services and assisted living. As a result, a Medicaid beneficiary may not have the care options available to others, and many people who could be cared for at home must enter a nursing home.

In summary, those who rely on Medicaid to pay for their long-term care lose their assets and their financial independence and have limited choices of types of care and facilities.

On the AARP web site, read the article "Medicaid: Paying for Nursing Home Care." To get there directly, go to *www.aarp.org/confacts/health/medicaidnurse.*

After you have done your reading and research, write down what you would say to help someone understand the disadvantages to relying on Medicaid to pay for long-term care.

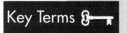

» What's Next

In the next chapter, we will look at how long-term care insurance helps meet long-term care needs, and we will examine the features of LTCI policies.

Key Terms

Average monthly private-pay rate

Community spouse

Countable asset

Eligibility limit

Estate recovery

Look-back period

Medicaid

Minimum monthly maintenance needs allowance

Nursing home eligible

Noncountable asset

Penalty period

Personal needs allowance

Spend down

Spousal impoverishment

Transfer of assets

» Review Questions

1. What is the purpose of the Medicaid program?

2. What role does the federal government play in the Medicaid program?

3. What role do state governments play in the Medicaid program?

4. What long-term care benefits does Medicaid provide?

5. What does it mean to "spend down" to become eligible for Medicaid?

6. What happens if a Medicaid applicant's countable assets are greater than the eligibility limit?

7. What are noncountable assets for purposes of Medicaid eligibility?

8. How does Medicaid treat the income of the spouse of a Medicaid applicant who is not also applying for Medicaid (a community spouse)?

9. Why is it not generally advantageous for a Medicaid applicant to transfer assets to family members?

10. How can being a Medicaid beneficiary affect one's choice of facilities?

» Answers

1. To pay for health care services for poor people of all ages.

2. It establishes broad guidelines for the operation of Medicaid and provides a majority of funding.

3. Each state administers its own program. It establishes (within federal guidelines) eligibility criteria; the type, amount, and duration of services its program pays for; and rates of payment for services. And it provides substantial funding for its program.

4. All state programs cover nursing home care, and they are also required to provide benefits for home health care for those who are nursing home eligible. Some states also pay benefits for home and community-based services for certain other Medicaid beneficiaries, but eligibility

may be restricted and benefits are limited. Most states do not cover care received in an assisted living residence.

5. People who are not poor when they first need long-term care use the assets they have accumulated over a lifetime to pay for long-term care until they have very little left, and they spend almost all their income on care. Then they meet Medicaid's eligibility limits and can receive benefits for Medicaid-covered services.

6. If the total value of a person's countable assets exceeds the eligibility limit, he is not eligible for Medicaid. To become eligible, he must spend all countable assets above the eligibility limit on care; illiquid assets, such as houses and vehicles, must be sold and the money spent on care.

7. Noncountable assets are those that Medicaid does not count in calculating whether the eligibility limit has been exceeded; they do not have to be sold to pay for care.

8. A community spouse who has her own sources of income does not have to spend that income on the care of the spouse receiving Medicaid benefits. In addition, if a community spouse's own monthly income is less than a floor amount, she can receive enough of the income of the spouse receiving Medicaid to make up the difference.

9. Because Medicaid imposes a penalty period—that is, when an individual makes a transfer of assets in which he receives less than the value of the assets 36 months or less before applying for Medicaid (60 months for transfers to a trust), Medicaid withholds benefits roughly equal in value to the assets transferred.

10. In most states, Medicaid pays long-term care facilities less for caring for Medicaid beneficiaries than they receive from private patients. Consequently, many in-demand nursing homes do not accept Medicaid patients, and most nursing homes that do accept them allocate only a limited number of beds to them, so that there is a long waiting list for Medicaid beds in the more popular facilities.

NOTES

1 AARP Public Policy Institute. 2003. *State Profiles: Reforming the Health Care System.*

2 Congressional Budget Office. April 2004. *Financing Long-Term Care for the Elderly.*

3 Georgetown University Long-Term Care Financing Project. July 2004. Fact sheet: "Medicaid and an Aging Population."

4 U.S. Department of Health and Human Services, Centers for Medicare and Medicaid Services. 2005.

5 Ibid.

6 Ibid.

7 Ibid.

8 U.S. Department of Health and Human Services, Centers for Medicare and Medicaid Services. 1996. *Transfers of Assets, 1996,* p. 1.

Long-Term Care Insurance

» What You Will Gain from This Chapter

As a result of the reading, research, and thinking you do in this chapter, you will be able to explain the advantages of long-term care insurance as a means of paying for long-term care, and you will be able to describe the features and options of LTCI policies.

» The Limitations of the Funding Methods Discussed So Far

In this chapter, we will look at another means of paying for long-term care—long-term care insurance. But first, let's review briefly the limitations and drawbacks of the methods we have examined so far.

Medicare and Medicare Supplement Insurance

The Medicare program pays for medical expenses of the elderly. Medicare provides some benefits for long-term care services, but these are very limited. For example, Medicare covers nursing home care, but only for short periods following hospitalization. Moreover, benefits for both nursing home care and home care are provided only to those needing skilled care to recover from an acute illness or injury. Medicare does not cover ongoing personal or supervisory care needed to cope with a chronic impairment. And neither Medicare supplement insurance nor Medicare Advantage plans provide any significant additional coverage for long-term care.

Medicaid

The Medicaid program does pay for long-term care services. However, those who are not indigent must deplete their life savings and assets before they can become eligible for Medicaid, and while receiving Medicaid benefits they must spend almost all their income on care. Moreover, because most state Medicaid programs focus on nursing home care and because Medicaid does not usually pay providers as much as they get from private patients, care options are often limited for Medicaid beneficiaries.

Savings and Assets

As we have seen, long-term care is expensive. It is not realistic to expect most Americans to be able to save the amount of money they would need to pay for long-term care, especially while trying to buy a home, save for their children's education, and fund their own retirement. And those who do rely on their own funds to pay for care must often deplete most or all of the assets they have spent a lifetime accumulating, leaving little or nothing for a comfortable retirement or for a surviving spouse or other heirs.

» Long-Term Care Insurance

To summarize the preceding section: The long-term care benefits of Medicare and Medicare supplement policies are very limited. If a person needs care for an extended time, she will have to deplete her assets. If this is not enough, she will have to go on Medicaid, with a sacrifice of care options.

This is a bleak picture. However, there is a solution—long-term care insurance. A person can purchase an LTCI policy, pay regular premiums of an amount she can afford, and in return, when she needs care, the policy will provide benefits to help pay for the services she requires.

There are several advantages to this method of funding long-term care costs:

■ The insured knows that when she needs care, there will be funds to help pay for it.

■ The policy's benefits will help preserve the insured's savings and assets.

■ The insured pays premiums of an amount that is known in advance and can be budgeted for, instead of paying the entire cost of care, the amount of which is unpredictable and could be very great.

■ The policy can cover a range of care options, allowing the insured to receive the services that meet her needs and enable her to age in place.

■ The policy's benefits can ensure access to high-quality care, not always available to those relying on Medicaid or limited personal funds.

Write down what you would say to help someone understand the advantages of long-term care insurance as a means of paying for long-term care and the disadvantages of the other payment methods we have discussed.

Thinking

_____

_____

_____

_____

_____

_____

_____

_____

_____

_____

_____

_____

» LTCI Policy Design and Options

Long-term care insurance policies vary considerably in coverage and cost. Some inexpensive policies provide only nursing home benefits, and for only two or three years. Other policies cost more but cover a wider variety of expenses, including assisted living and home health care, and pay benefits for a longer time.

Differences in coverage result both from different policy designs and from optional features. The design and options of LTCI policies can best be understood in terms of a set of questions and choices, which we will address in the remainder of this chapter.

Some of the policy provisions discussed below are mandated by the Health Insurance Portability and Accountability Act of 1996 (HIPAA), and others are required by the Long-Term Care Insurance Model Act and Model Regulation developed by the National Association of Insurance Commissioners (NAIC), which have been adopted, in whole or in part, by most states.

What Settings Are Covered?

As we have discussed, there are many settings in which long-term care can take place, such as the home, an adult day center, an assisted living residence, a nursing home, and others. Many policies offer comprehensive benefits covering all or most of these settings, while others reimburse only for care in a nursing home, or only for care in some sort of facility, or only for home care.

Some policies that cover several settings pay equal benefit amounts for all settings. Other policies provide different benefits for different settings, typically paying lower amounts for services provided at home.

Research

If you are involved in the sale or administration of long-term care insurance, as you go through this chapter look at the policies you handle and examine their features. At this point, for example, look at the settings these policies cover.

If you are a consumer, as you go through the chapter consider your own circumstances and make decisions about the policy features that are important to you.

When Are Benefits Paid?

To receive benefits under an LTCI policy, an insured must meet at least one of certain conditions stipulated in the policy, known as **benefit triggers**. There are two common types:

- **Physical (or functional) impairment**—the insured's physical condition prevents her from performing a specified number of activities of daily living (usually two or three).

- **Cognitive impairment**—the insured suffers from a serious cognitive condition such that close supervision is necessary to protect her health and safety.

These benefit triggers are used because they are the most reliable indicators of when someone needs long-term care and because they can be objectively measured, thus ensuring accurate and consistent determinations of eligibility for benefits.

For an LTCI policy to be deemed tax-qualified under HIPAA (see below), it must meet certain requirements in relation to benefit triggers:

- HIPAA establishes six standard ADLs (bathing, dressing, toileting, transferring, continence, and eating) and precisely defines them. Tax-qualified policies must include at least five of these six and must use the HIPAA definitions. Also, they must define a physical impairment as the inability to perform at least two of the standard ADLs without substantial assistance from another person.

- **Substantial assistance** must be defined as either hands-on or stand-by assistance. If an insured needs **hands-on assistance** with an ADL, she cannot perform the ADL without the physical involvement of another person; if she needs **stand-by assistance**, she can usually perform the ADL herself but needs another person present who can step in to prevent injury if something goes wrong.

- A tax-qualified policy must include a **90-day certification requirement**— that is, a licensed health care practitioner (a physician or nurse) must certify that a physical impairment is expected to last at least 90 days. This provision is necessary because LTCI benefits are not intended for those unable to bathe themselves or dress for a short time while they are recovering from an illness or injury. There is no such requirement for a cognitive impairment, as such impairments are rarely temporary.

■ To qualify for benefits on a cognitive basis, an insured must suffer from a **severe cognitive impairment**, defined by HIPAA as a loss of or deterioration in intellectual capacity that is comparable to and includes Alzheimer's disease and similar forms of irreversible dementia and that can be reliably measured by clinical evidence and standardized tests.

The benefit triggers of some policies are more difficult to meet than those of others. Some policies require the inability to perform only two ADLs while others require three or more. Under some policies the insured must need hands-on assistance, under others only stand-by assistance.

How Long Is the Elimination Period?

An **elimination period** (sometimes called a **waiting period**) is an amount of time that must elapse after an insured meets a benefit trigger before he begins to receive benefits. In other words, when an insured begins to need long-term care services, he normally has to pay for them himself for a certain time before benefits begin. Typical elimination period options are 30 and 90 days, but they can range from zero to 180 days or more, depending on the insurer and applicable state regulations.

The purpose of elimination periods is to offer insureds a way to hold down premium costs—the longer the elimination period an insured chooses, the less the insurer is likely to pay in benefits and the lower the premium it must charge. On the other hand, the longer the elimination period, the more the insured will pay out of pocket if he needs care. For example, Mr. Phillips has a 90-day elimination period. He goes into a nursing home and must pay for the first 90 days of care himself. At $150 per day, this comes to $13,500. If his elimination period were 30 days, he would pay only $4,500 before he begins to receive benefits.

How elimination periods function varies:

■ Under some policies, the elimination period starts when the insured both meets a benefit trigger and begins receiving long-term care services covered by the policy; under others, it starts as soon as the insured meets a benefit trigger, whether he is receiving covered services or not. (He might be receiving unpaid care from a family member.)

■ For most policies today the elimination period must be satisfied only once during the life of the policy, but for some policies it must be satisfied for each period during which the insured receives care.

■ Most newer policies allow days counting toward the elimination period to accumulate over the life of the policy. But under some policies if the insured has not accumulated the required number of days within a certain time (such as two years), he must begin again.

Research

Sales and insurer personnel: Study the policies you handle, and find out their benefit triggers and elimination period options.

Consumers: Consider your own needs and preferences in these areas.

Thinking

After you have done your reading and research, write down what you would say to help someone understand benefit triggers and elimination periods.

_____

_____

_____

_____

_____

_____

_____

How Much Are Benefits?

 Long-term care insurance policies typically have a set dollar amount of benefit per day or month. A purchaser selects a **benefit amount** ranging from $40 to $500 per day or $1,500 to $12,000 per month. Most LTCI policies use the benefit amount as a limit and pay covered expenses incurred by the insured up to that amount. A few pay the benefit amount regardless of the actual expenses of the insured.

As noted above, some policies pay the same benefit amount for different settings while others pay different amounts. When benefits differ with setting, the daily benefit for home care is often defined as a percentage of the daily benefit for nursing home care. The home care benefit is almost always at least 50 percent, and some recommend at least 75 percent or (if possible) 100 percent.

The benefit amount a purchaser chooses should be based on how much is charged by nursing homes, assisted living residences, and home health care agencies in his area. It should be kept in mind that actual charges may exceed stated daily rates. For example, a nursing home may charge extra for drugs, supplies, and special services, and this can increase costs by several hundred dollars each month.

In selecting a benefit amount, the purchaser should also consider how much of the cost of long-term care (if any) he is willing and able to pay out of his own pocket. Some people prefer to rely on insurance to cover only a portion of long-term care expenses and to pay the rest out of their income and assets.

The daily or monthly benefit amount has perhaps the greatest impact on the amount of the premium. Obviously, the greater the benefit, the higher the premium.

How Long Will Benefits Be Paid?

The **benefit period** of an insurance policy is the total amount of time benefits will be paid. Common benefit periods for LTCI policies are two, three, four, five, and ten years, and unlimited lifetime coverage. Normally in long-term care insurance, if an insured receives benefits during different periods, the total time he receives benefits counts against his benefit period. For example, Mr. Glass has a policy with a benefit period of three years (36 months). He enters a nursing home and receives benefits for 14 months. He returns home and receives no benefits for two months. He then goes back into the nursing home and receives benefits for nine months. Mr. Glass has used 23 months of his benefit period and has 13 months left, after which he will no longer receive benefits. Note that there can be exceptions to this system — see "Restoration of benefits" below.

Most policies today, instead of a benefit period, have a **maximum lifetime benefit** (sometimes called a **pool of money**). With these policies, benefits are provided until the total amount paid reaches the maximum amount. For example, Ms. Bushnell selects a maximum benefit amount of $150,000 with a daily benefit of $150. If she spends the daily maximum on care, benefits will last 1,000 days. However, if Ms. Bushnell's care costs less than $150 a day (as might be the case with limited home health care), her pool of money will last for more than 1,000 days.

Like the benefit amount and the elimination period, the benefit period or maximum lifetime benefit is a major factor in the cost of the premium. The longer the benefit period or the larger the pool of money, the higher the premium. How much is needed in total benefits? It is impossible to say, as no one can predict how long any one person will need long-term care. According to the National Center for Health Statistics, the average nursing home stay is 2.44 years, but over 13.8 percent of all stays exceed five years.[1]

Research

Sales and insurer personnel: Study the policies you handle, and find out their daily or monthly benefit amounts and benefit periods or maximum lifetime benefits.

Consumers: Consider your own needs and preferences in these areas.

Thinking

After you have done your reading and research, write down what you would say to help someone understand benefit amounts, benefit periods, and maximum lifetime benefits.

_____

_____

_____

_____

_____

_____

_____

_____

_____

_____

_____

_____

_____

_____

What Inflation Protection Is There?

Long-term care costs have been rising for many years, and this trend is expected to continue. Inflation protection ensures that the daily or monthly benefit (and usually also the maximum lifetime benefit) increases along with costs so that care can be paid for when it is needed in the future.

Therefore, although it adds to the premium price, inflation protection can be one of the most important features of an LTCI policy, especially for those purchasing coverage years before they expect to need benefits.

With **automatic inflation protection**, benefit amounts are regularly increased at a set rate with no action by the insured required and no corresponding increase in premium. Two common automatic options are:

- **The 5 percent simple rate.** Benefit amounts are increased by 5 percent of the initial amount each year. For example, a daily benefit of $100 would rise to $105 in the second year, $110 in the third year, and so on.

- **The 5 percent compound rate.** The increase is compounded, like compound interest in a bank account. In other words, each year there is a 5 percent increase based not on the initial benefit amount (as with the simple rate) but on the previous year's amount. This leads to a snowballing effect, such that, although in the early years of the policy the increases in benefits are not much greater than with the 5 percent simple option, in later years they are substantially greater.

The simple rate option costs less, since in the long run it results in a significantly smaller increase in benefits. However, as noted, during the early years of the policy, benefit increases are almost as great as with the compound rate. Therefore, the simple rate option offers less expensive inflation protection that is probably sufficient for a person who is likely to need benefits fairly soon, such as someone who is already elderly when he buys a policy. On the other hand, the compound rate option provides better protection when the need for benefits is not expected to occur for many years, as would be the case with younger people. (In tax-qualified policies, the 5 percent compound option must be offered to all applicants, although they may choose not to take it.)

In most LTCI policies, automatic inflation increases continue for the life of the policy. However, a few policies have limitations: some impose a cap on benefits of double the original amount, and others stop automatic increases after 20 years or when the insured reaches a specified age.

In addition to automatic increases, there is another approach to inflation protection—the **guaranteed purchase option**. Under this option, at set intervals (such as every year or every three years) the insured is given the opportunity to increase the benefit amount, with a corresponding increase in the premium. If the insured accepts such an offer, the premium increase is based on the amount of additional benefits and the insured's age. If an insured declines a certain number of these offers, the insurer may discontinue them. An insurer may also decline to make an offer if the insured makes a claim a certain amount of time before the offer is scheduled to occur.

The guaranteed purchase option does not usually work well for those buying a policy when they are relatively young. After many years, increasing the benefit amount enough to keep up with inflation requires larger and larger premium increases, sometimes eventually making the policy unaffordable. Automatic inflation protection, on the other hand, gives the insured a known, budgetable premium.

Finally, some purchasers address the problem of inflation by simply selecting a higher benefit amount than is initially needed. For example, if local nursing home rates are currently $150 a day, a daily benefit of $250 might be selected in anticipation of rising costs. This of course adds to the premium price. And if the insured is relatively young, it may not solve the inflation problem, since long-term care costs may have tripled, or more, years from now when the insured needs care.

What Nonforfeiture Option Is Available?

A **nonforfeiture** option allows an insured who stops paying premiums and lets her policy lapse to receive something for the premiums she has already paid. This could be a cash payment or continuation of coverage for a limited time.

Under a cash surrender value option or return of premium option, a cash payment is made.

- The **cash surrender value option** is triggered by the surrender (termination) of the policy by the insured while she is still living. The amount is based on the total amount of premiums she paid over the life of the policy, in some cases reduced by the amount of any claims paid.

- The **return of premium option** is triggered by the death of the insured, and the payment is made to her estate or designated beneficiary. The amount is based on premiums paid and, for some policies, the insured's age at death. Some policies do not pay a benefit if claims have been made, or the amount of benefit is reduced.

The **shortened benefit period option** has been adopted by the NAIC in its Model Regulation. Under this option, an insured who quits paying premiums retains the right to benefits equal in amount to the total premiums she has paid (without interest), or 30 days of benefits if this is greater, provided the policy was in force three years or more. For example, Mrs. Wilson purchases a policy with an annual premium of $1,200. Seven years later, after she has paid a total of $8,400 in premiums, she lets the policy lapse. She is entitled to $8,400 in benefits, and two years later, when she enters a nursing home, she receives the policy's daily benefit ($100) for 84 days. (The name "shortened benefit period" is used because until the insured has used up her accumulated benefits, all of the provisions of the policy remain in force, except that the benefit period is effectively reduced.)

Note that a nonforfeiture option adds to premium cost.

What Provision Is There for Renewal?

By law, all LTCI policies must be either guaranteed renewable or noncancellable. If a policy is **guaranteed renewable**, the insurer must renew the policy (that is, continue it year after year) as long as the insured pays the premiums. The insurer may not decline to renew because of the insured's age, health, claim history, or for any other reason. Furthermore, an insurer cannot increase the premium on a single guaranteed renewable policy, only on a group of policies and only with the approval of the state insurance department. Approval is generally granted only when the claims experience of the group has been worse than projected.

A **noncancellable** policy, like a guaranteed renewable policy, cannot be terminated by the insurer unless the insured stops paying premiums. But unlike a guaranteed renewable policy, a noncancellable policy's premium can never be increased under any circumstances. Noncancellable LTCI policies cost more than guaranteed renewable policies and are becoming quite rare.

Research

Sales and insurer personnel: Study the policies you handle and find out what inflation protection and nonforfeiture options are available for them.

Consumers: Consider your own needs and preferences in these areas.

Thinking

After you have done your reading and research, write down what you would say to help someone understand inflation protection and nonforfeiture options and the guaranteed renewable provision.

_____

_____

_____

_____

_____

_____

_____

_____

_____

_____

_____

_____

_____

_____

Is the Policy Tax-Qualified?

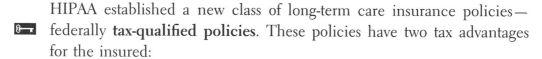

HIPAA established a new class of long-term care insurance policies—federally **tax-qualified policies**. These policies have two tax advantages for the insured:

■ Benefits paid by tax-qualified policies are not normally considered taxable income. An exception is policies that pay the benefit amount even if the actual long-term care expenses of the insured are less, in which case benefits that exceed a certain limit may be taxed.

■ Premiums paid by an individual on a tax-qualified policy may in certain circumstances be partially tax-deductible. A taxpayer may include in her itemized deductions premiums up to a maximum amount based on her age. If the amount of LTCI premiums (up to the allowed maximum) and other deductible medical expenses add up to more than 7.5 percent of the taxpayer's adjusted gross income (AGI), the amount in excess of 7.5 percent of AGI is deductible from taxable income.

To be tax-qualified, policies going into effect on or after January 1, 1997, must fulfill certain requirements:

■ They must be labeled as tax-qualified.
■ They must contain certain consumer protection provisions.
■ Their benefit triggers must meet certain standards, as discussed above.
■ They must cover only qualified long-term care services provided as part of a plan of care prescribed by a licensed health care practitioner.

Most LTCI policies issued before January 1, 1997, are **"grandfathered."** That is, because these policies were already in force when the new requirements were established, they are deemed tax-qualified even though they may not fulfill all the requirements that new policies must meet.

Are There Additional Features and Options?

Many LTCI policies have other provisions and options in addition to the ones already discussed. These include the following:

■ **Spousal discount.** Many insurers offer discounts on premiums ranging from 20 to 40 percent if both husband and wife purchase long-term care coverage. Some insurers in some states extend the spousal discount to same-sex couples, other committed couples not legally married, and same-generation family members living together. Many companies grant a smaller discount to any married person, even if her spouse does not also purchase coverage, on the grounds that married people can help care for each other and so are less likely to need paid long-term care services.

■ **Waiver of premium.** The insured does not have to pay premiums while he is receiving benefits. Under some policies, this applies only when the insured is in a nursing home or other facility, while for others it also applies when he is receiving care at home.

■ **Survivor benefit.** If an insured dies and a spouse covered by the same policy or a linked policy survives, the spouse will continue to receive coverage without paying premiums. For this waiver of premium to occur, the policy must have been in force for a specified number of years (often seven to ten), and for some policies no claims may have been filed.

■ **Alternate plan of care** (also called emerging trends benefit, alternative care benefit, supplementary care benefit, and other names). This feature allows for flexibility in services covered. For example, under an alternate plan of care provision, a policy might pay for home enhancements such as bathroom alterations, handrails, and ramps that make it possible for a person to safely remain at home instead of entering a nursing home. In addition, newly developed long-term care services can be covered without the need of amending the policy to specifically include them. Thus the flexibility afforded by this provision makes it easier for the insured to age in place and keeps the policy from becoming obsolete.

■ **Respite care coverage.** Coverage of respite care provides for the hiring of a paid caregiver for a short period so that an unpaid caregiver (such as a family member) can take a break. This could be a few hours off to go shopping or a week or two for a vacation.

■ **Informal caregiver benefits.** Some policies pay a benefit when care is provided to the insured by a family member or other informal caregiver. Others pay for the training of an informal caregiver.

- **Homemaker services and transportation coverage.** Help with household chores and transportation to medical appointments and shopping may be covered. Some policies pay for these services only if other home health care services (such as those provided by a home health aide, nurse, or therapist) are needed. For other policies, the only requirement is that a benefit trigger be met.

- **Impairment reinstatement provision.** With this provision, if a cognitive or physical impairment causes the insured to neglect to pay premiums and allow the policy to lapse, the insurer will reinstate coverage without underwriting, provided proof of the impairment is submitted and the premium is paid within a specified amount of time after the lapse notice.

- **Third-party notification.** The insured can designate another person, such as an adult child, to whom the insurer must send a copy of a lapse notice when the insured does not pay the premium. Like impairment reinstatement, this protects an insured who may inadvertently let a policy lapse during a period of physical or cognitive impairment. This provision must be included in tax-qualified policies.

- **Bed reservation benefit.** Because of the high demand for nursing home beds, a nursing home patient can lose his bed while he is in the hospital or away visiting family. Bed reservation benefits pay the nursing home (and in most cases an assisted living residence) to hold the insured's bed during his absence.

- **Care coordinator.** Under many policies, the insurer pays for the services of a care coordinator or provides one itself without charge. A care coordinator is a person who works on behalf of the insured to see that he receives the best care possible and gets the most out of the benefits the policy provides. For example, a care coordinator can identify the best available providers of the services the insured needs. A care coordinator may also send regular care reports to family members, and having one is especially helpful when family members do not live nearby.

- **Restoration of benefits.** This provision can restore a partially depleted pool of money or benefit period. If an insured uses some of the dollars in his pool of money or some of the days in his benefit period, but then receives no benefits for a specified period (generally six to twelve months), the dollars or days he has used are restored to his original pool of money or benefit period. (For example, a person with a 60-month benefit period might receive benefits for 10 months, then receive no benefits for a year, and have his original 60 months restored, as if he had never made a claim.)

Research

Sales and insurer personnel: Study the policies you handle, and find out which of the features and options discussed above are available with them.

Consumers: Consider your own needs and preferences in these areas.

Thinking

After you have done your reading and research, write down what you would say to help someone understand the features and options discussed above.

_____

_____

_____

_____

_____

_____

_____

_____

_____

_____

_____

_____

_____

_____

» How Much Is the Premium?

The factors with the greatest impact on the amount of the premium of an LTCI policy are the following:

- **The benefit amount.** The greater the daily or monthly benefit amount, the higher the premium.

- **The maximum lifetime benefit.** A larger pool of money is more expensive than a smaller pool of money.

- **The benefit period.** The longer the benefit period, the higher the premium.

- **The elimination period.** The longer the elimination period, the lower the premium.

- **Home health care.** Policies that provide home health care benefits are more expensive than those that do not. The home health care benefit amount can range from 50 percent of the nursing home benefit to 100 percent; the higher the percentage, the higher the premium.

- **Inflation protection.** Automatic inflation protection increases the premium. A simple rate option is cheaper than a compound rate. There may or may not be a charge for adding a guaranteed purchase option to a policy. Choosing a higher benefit amount than initially needed as a hedge against inflation adds to premium cost.

- **Nonforfeiture.** This option comes at an additional cost.

After you have done your reading, write down what you would say to help someone understand the factors affecting the premium amount.

Thinking

_____

_____

_____

_____

_____

_____

_____

_____

_____

_____

_____

» What's Next

In the next chapter, we will look at the various means of spreading information about the need for long-term care and the role of long-term care insurance in paying for it.

Key Terms

Alternate plan of care	Impairment reinstatement
Automatic inflation protection	Informal caregiver benefits
Bed reservation benefit	Maximum lifetime benefit
Benefit amount	Ninety-day certification requirement
Benefit period	Noncancellable
Benefit trigger	Nonforfeiture
Care coordinator	Physical impairment
Cash surrender value option	Pool of money
Cognitive impairment	Restoration of benefits
Elimination period	Return of premium option
Functional impairment	Severe cognitive impairment
Grandfathered	Shortened benefit period option
Guaranteed purchase option	Spousal discount
Guaranteed renewable	Stand-by assistance
Hands-on assistance	

Key Terms 🔑	Substantial assistance	Third-party notification
	Survivor benefit	Waiting period
	Tax-qualified policy	Waiver of premium

» Review Questions

1. What are the advantages of long-term care insurance in providing for long-term care expenses?

   There will be funds to pay for LTC when needed.
   Savings/Assets will be preserved

2. How do LTCI policies differ in terms of care settings covered?

   ① Some offer care for all (home, adult day center, assisted living residence, nursing home)
   ② only nursing home facilities ③ home care

3. What are the two common types of benefit triggers?

   physical impairment

   cognitive impairment

4. In what two ways can "substantial assistance" with ADLs be defined?

   hands on — phys involv w/ other)
   Stand by — somebody who can step in

5. What is an elimination period?

   Time passes after trigger B4 receive benes

6. On what basis should a purchaser select his benefit amount?

   how much in his area
   how much ably willing to pay

7. What is a benefit period?

Tot Amt time benes pd.

8. How does a maximum lifetime benefit (pool of money) work?

benes pd till Tot max reached

9. Would simple rate inflation protection be more appropriate for an older or for a younger person? Why?

*Same each year
Older
Costs less*

*in early years bene
increases just as much*

because something for prems pd

10. What are the two ways an insured might be compensated under a nonforfeiture option?

1. Cash Surrender value option   value

2. Ret prem opt. → death

cash → cont cov long term.

11. What does a guaranteed renewable provision do?

*must renew as long as insured pays premiums
increase only on group w/ approval of ST ins dept.*

12. What are the tax advantages of a tax-qualified policy?

*benes pd not tx inc.
prem. pd tax deductible*

13. What does an impairment reinstatement provision do?

Reinstate covg if person can't pay because of impairment

14. What does a restoration of benefits provision do?

Use LTCI for a period - then not use for a period - ones used will be given back

15. What are the major factors that determine the premium rate of an LTCI policy?

- elim period
- home helth cr
- infl. protection
- bene amt
- max lifetime bene
- bene period
- nonforfeiture

» Answers

1. There will be funds to help pay for care when it is needed, the policy's benefits will help preserve the insured's savings and assets, the insured pays premiums of an amount that is known in advance and can be budgeted for, the policy can cover a range of care options, and the policy's benefits can ensure access to high-quality care.

2. Some policies cover a range of settings, while others reimburse only for care in a nursing home, or only for care in some sort of facility, or only for home care.

3. Physical impairment and cognitive impairment.

4. In a tax-qualified policy, substantial assistance must be defined as either hands-on or stand-by assistance. If an insured needs hands-on assistance with an ADL, she cannot perform the ADL without the physical involvement of another person; if she needs stand-by assistance, she can usually perform the ADL herself but needs another person present who can step in to prevent injury if something goes wrong.

5. An amount of time that must elapse after an insured meets a benefit trigger before he begins to receive benefits.

6. On how much is charged by nursing homes, assisted living residences, and home health care agencies in his area. How much of the cost of long-term care (if any) the purchaser is willing and able to pay out of his own pocket should also be taken into account.

7. The total amount of time benefits will be paid.

8. Benefits are provided until the total amount paid reaches the maximum amount.

9. An older person, because it may be sufficient for a person who is likely to need benefits fairly soon.

10. A cash payment or continuation of coverage for a limited time.

11. If a policy is guaranteed renewable, the insurer must renew the policy as long as the insured pays the premiums. In addition, the insurer cannot increase the premium on a single guaranteed renewable policy, only on a group of policies and only with the approval of the state insurance department.

12. Benefits paid by tax-qualified policies are not normally considered taxable income, and premiums paid by an individual on a tax-qualified policy may in certain circumstances be partially tax-deductible.

13. If a cognitive or physical impairment causes the insured to neglect to pay premiums and allow the policy to lapse, the insurer will reinstate coverage without underwriting.

14. If an insured uses some of his pool of money or benefit period but then receives no benefits for a specified period, the original pool of money or benefit period is restored.

15. The benefit amount, benefit period or maximum lifetime benefit, elimination period, home health care benefits, inflation protection, and nonforfeiture.

NOTE

1 Jones, A., National Center for Health Statistics. 2002. "The National Nursing Home Survey: 1999 Summary," *Vital Health Stat* 13(152).

 7

Spreading
The Word

- Ways of Getting Out the Message
- Face-to-Face Meetings
- Telephone Calls
- Direct Mail
- Print Advertising
- Broadcast Media
- The Internet
- Seminars

» What You Will Gain from This Chapter

As a result of the reading, research, and thinking you do in this chapter, you will be able to describe seven ways of disseminating information on long-term care needs and long-term care insurance.

» Why This Information Is Important to You

In the first half of this book, we learned why long-term care insurance is the best way to finance long-term care for many people. We will now look at ways to share this knowledge with others. Specifically, in the next few chapters, we will examine how insurance sales professionals can educate people about the need for long-term care insurance and sell them policies.

Clearly, this information is oriented toward insurance agents and brokers and the sales personnel of insurance companies. However, those with positions in other areas of insurance also need to be familiar with the LTCI sales process. And those outside the insurance field, including health care professionals and consumers, will find it useful to know how people learn about long-term care insurance.

In this chapter and those that follow, salespeople will gain information that will enable them to:

- make better use of their time,

- increase their productivity, and
- gain greater career satisfaction by reaching qualified prospects seeking the type of information and services they can provide.

Other insurer personnel will gain:

- a better understanding of the issues faced by the field sales force in selling long-term care insurance,
- information that can be used to increase both home office and field productivity,
- knowledge that can be tapped in preparing sales support materials, and
- insight into ways of better providing information to customers and prospects in direct dealings with them.

» Ways of Getting Out the Message

There are several of ways of informing people about long-term care needs and the role that long-term care insurance can play in meeting those needs. These include:

- face-to-face meetings,
- telephone calls,
- direct mail campaigns,
- print advertisements,
- broadcast media campaigns,
- Internet communications, and
- seminars.

All of these methods can be highly effective. They each can also prove to be an ineffective use of valuable time and resources. What marks the difference between success and failure?

The answer lies in knowing *how* to use each method and *when* to use it. In other words, a method is effective if it is professionally executed and employed at an appropriate time. In the sections that follow, we will offer guidance on the use of each of these ways of spreading the long-term care message.

» Face-to-Face Meetings

A face-to-face, one-on-one meeting gives an insurance salesperson an in-depth understanding of an individual's particular circumstances. Specifically, the advantages of face-to-face meetings with sales prospects include the following:

- The salesperson can learn in detail about the prospect's needs and goals.
- She can discuss a variety of options with the prospect and tailor a policy to his circumstances.
- She can learn about any obstacles to paying premiums and suggest ways to overcome them.
- She can uncover any potential underwriting problems.

However, meeting with prospects one by one is very time-consuming. This expenditure of time may be productive and necessary at some stages in the sales process, but at the beginning, when the goal is to provide general information, it is not. Other methods, such as seminars, mailings, and advertising, are more efficient for this purpose. In addition, an agent who holds face-to-face meetings early in the sales process will often spend valuable time with people who have no interest in the product or who are not **qualified prospects** (individuals who are insurable and can afford the coverage).

» Telephone Calls

A telephone call to a sales prospect the salesperson does not already know is referred to as a **cold call**. Cold calling is now subject to some severe restrictions, the Federal Trade Commission's "Do Not Call" rules, and salespeople must become familiar with these regulations and adhere to them. Even when, under certain circumstances, cold calling is allowed, it can be very time-consuming and can result in expensive telephone bills. Because of these restrictions and drawbacks, cold calling should be used as a supplementary means of finding new prospects, not the primary method.

Telephone calls to people the agent already knows and to referrals who have contacted the agent are known as **warm calls**. Warm calls can be an effective means for both agents and sales-support personnel to:

- maintain contact with prospects once initial contact has taken place,
- set up appointments for sales interviews requested by prospects,
- confirm attendance and verify information with prospects who have accepted seminar invitations, and
- maintain contact with established clients (to discuss current coverage, periodic reviews, and suggested updates).

» Direct Mail

Direct mail campaigns offer sales agents and sales-support personnel a way of reaching many people for a relatively small expenditure per person in terms of both time and money.

The key to a successful direct mail campaign is proper targeting—that is, making sure that those who receive the mailing are likely prospects. Obviously, if an LTCI mailing is sent to a list of people who do not find long-term care insurance of interest or who cannot afford it, the mailing will yield few prospects, and the time and money spent on the development and production of materials and on postage will be wasted.

A series of mailings to the same group of prospects is generally more successful than a single mailing. Such multiple mailings can help establish the salesperson in the minds of prospects as a source of information and products related to long-term care, and they increase the probability that a mailing will reach a prospect at a time when he is most receptive.

Self-Generated Lists

A mailing can be sent to a **self-generated list**. This is a list created by an agent and made up of current clients, referrals, and other people in the community she knows. Mailing to a self-generated list has certain advantages. Because the agent knows the people on her list, she can identify those who are likely to be interested and qualified and mail only to them.

And because the recipients of the mailing know the agent, the response is likely to be fairly good.

On the other hand, the use of self-generated lists does have limitations. Since the agent is sending material largely to people she already knows, the potential for uncovering new clients is limited. And an agent's pool of contacts is usually too small to generate a very large list.

Purchased Lists

An agent can also purchase a mailing list. This allows her to mail to people she does not already know and so reach new clients. And the agent can target her mailing by choosing a list of people with characteristics that make them likely prospects. For example, an agent might buy a list of people living in her area, over 40 years old, and engaged in certain well-paying professions. On the other hand, since the people on a purchased list do not know the agent, there may be less response than with a self-generated list.

Some lists do not have to be purchased; they are available to the public. For those looking for mailing lists, we offer the following pointers:

- Have a **prospect profile** in mind—that is, know what sort of person you are trying to reach (your **target prospect**) and what characteristics that person has. This will make it easier to find a list that contains such people.

- Think about how your target prospects might be identified. What magazines do they read? What conferences do they attend? What leisure activities do they pursue? Lists are often made up of magazine subscribers, conference attendees, etc.

- Consider using a **list broker**. This is a person whose business is selling and renting mailing lists. He has access to lists that are not generally available to the public, and he can also provide expertise. For example, a list broker is familiar with the various lists available and knows which are likely to best meet an agent's needs, which are regularly updated and which are not, how well different lists draw, and who else is using a particular list.

■ Visit your local business library. It should have reference sources, such as *Standard Rates and Data,* that provide basic information about the types of lists available and the names of list brokers. Even if you are already working with a list broker, this knowledge will allow you to better understand the role and capabilities of your broker.

■ Consider renting a list instead of buying it. Buying a list means that the list is yours to use as often as you want for as long as you want; renting means that you have the right to use the list one time, or as many times as you pay for. However, when you rent, once you gain a response from a name on the list, the name becomes your own. And it is typically cheaper to rent than to buy.

■ Realize that lists become dated quickly. People move, their interests change, some die. This is another reason that renting often makes better sense, as updating the list is the owner's responsibility.

Research

Visit your local business library. Look for mailing lists available to the public and choose one that could be used for a direct mail campaign on long-term care insurance. Also, find a list broker in your area.

Develop a prospect profile for a mailing about long-term care insurance.

Thinking

Write down why you chose the list you did in the above research exercise.

_____

_____

_____

_____

_____

_____

Call the list broker you found about possible lists you might use that fit the prospect profile you have developed. Write down the information provided by the list broker on list size, minimum purchase rules, and sources.

_____

_____

_____

_____

_____

_____

» Print Advertising

Despite increased use of the Internet, many people still rely on print media for information. For example, most LTCI prospects regularly read either a local or national newspaper. This makes print advertising a viable means for an agent to spread the message about his products, expertise, and company. For what is often a fairly reasonable price, he can reach a large audience and establish his professional presence in the community.

Advertising of course costs money, and the development of an effective advertisement requires both money and expertise. An insurer's home office may be able to provide both.

The choice of publication is key—advertising in the wrong publication can result in the message failing to reach the intended audience and the money spent being wasted. Advertising in a well-respected local newspaper is generally preferable. Not only does a local paper cost less, but its readership is concentrated in the agent's area of activity.

As with direct mail, a series of advertisements is more effective than a single one, as it increases the likelihood a prospect will see an ad when he is receptive, and it helps establish the salesperson in the community.

Research

Contact the home office or regional office of your carrier. Find out if they have a media kit that includes a sample print advertisement. If such a kit is available, order it and review the materials.

Contact the advertising representative of your local newspaper and ask for circulation information and advertising rates.

Thinking

After you have done your research, write down the answers to the following questions:

■ How could you use a company-provided media kit in developing a print advertisement for your local newspaper, and what compliance steps must you take to gain company approval of your efforts?

_____

_____

_____

_____

■ How much would you have to pay to run a quarter-page advertisement in a local newspaper?

_____

_____

_____

_____

» Broadcast Media

Broadcast media advertising enables a salesperson to reach a large audience of potential prospects and establish her professional presence in the community. The problem is that costs are usually high. However, in some areas the rates of local radio stations and cable television channels are low enough to make an advertising campaign feasible. An agent can also make use of broadcast media without paying a cent by appearing as a guest on a local program. Such programs are often looking for people with expertise to share.

» The Internet

Most people associate Internet use with the young, so one might not think it a particularly good means of reaching LTCI prospects. However, older people are becoming increasingly web-savvy, and many younger people have concerns about long-term care either for themselves or for family members. For these reasons, agents and home office personnel need to consider using the Internet for spreading the long-term care insurance message.

The web offers the following advantages:

■ It is a low-cost way of establishing initial contact with prospects.

■ It is a low-cost means of educating prospects about long-term care insurance.

■ It is a time-efficient way of maintaining contact with clients and prospects.

LTCI salespeople can use the Internet in several ways:

■ A salesperson can establish her own web site. There are now providers who will create a customized web site for an agent or add a personalized touch to a ready-made site. An agent should always make sure her site is in full compliance with the requirements of her company and state regulations.

■ There are web sites that sell Internet-generated leads to salespeople. These may be exclusive, new leads or older, "used" leads (people who expressed an interest or were contacted but who never took any action).

■ A salesperson can list herself and/or advertise with Internet search engines. Typically, every time an Internet information seeker clicks on a salesperson's web site directly from a list generated by a search engine, the salesperson pays an agreed-upon fee. Often a salesperson's position in a search engine result list depends on the amount she pays per click. With many programs, the salesperson can limit her expenditures by setting up a daily or monthly budget amount; when this amount is reached, the salesperson is temporarily taken off the search engine result list. A salesperson can also refine her participation in a search engine by choosing a certain geographic area or specific key words in whose search result list she wants to be included.

It should be realized that using the Internet is not without costs. Establishing and maintaining a web site requires money, as does buying placement on a search engine. And dealing with e-mail messages and information requests takes time.

» Seminars

Seminar selling is a marketing approach in which a knowledgeable sales professional makes a classroom-style presentation on a topic of interest to a group of prospects, with opportunities for one-on-one follow-up meetings in which selling can take place.

Seminar selling enables agents to:

- meet with a sizable number of people at the same time,
- get to know those people in a nonthreatening environment and establish rapport and trust,
- identify those who are qualified prospects, and
- obtain appointments for individual sales interviews.

Seminar selling can also help build the professional reputation of an agent and company in a community and create marketing buzz about a product.

It should be kept in mind, however, that a seminar program that is poorly planned and conducted can result in low attendance, the identification of few qualified prospects, and minimal sales despite substantial out-of-pocket costs. It can also damage the presenter's professional reputation in the community.

Seminar selling is actually combined with the other methods discussed in this chapter. First, prospects are attracted to a seminar by means of direct mail, telephoning, or advertising. Next, in the seminar, the salesperson educates prospects on long-term care and long-term care insurance. Then, in face-to-face meetings, the salesperson sells the product. In the following chapter, we will examine how a seminar selling campaign is conducted.

» What's Next

In the next chapter, we will examine how LTCI seminars are organized and conducted.

Key Terms

Cold call	Self-generated list
List broker	Seminar selling
Prospect profile	Target prospect
Qualified prospect	Warm call

» Review Questions

1. What are the ways of spreading the word about long-term care needs and long-term care insurance?

   face to face, telephone, direct mail, print ads, media, internet, seminars

2. What are the advantages of face-to-face meetings?

   + learn needs & goals
   + discuss options & tailor a policy approp.
   + discuss ways to overcome obstacles paying plan.
   + can uncover underwriting probs

3. What are the disadvantages of face-to-face meetings in the early stages of the sales process?

   time consuming

4. What are the drawbacks of cold calling?

Severe restrictions
time consuming
expensive telephone bills

5. What is the key to a successful direct mail campaign?

6. What are the advantages and disadvantages of using a self-generated list?

7. What is the key to a successful print advertising campaign?

8. In making use of broadcast media, how can the problem of cost be overcome?

9. What is seminar selling?

10. What are the advantages of seminar selling?

» Answers

1. Face-to-face meetings, telephone calls, direct mail campaigns, print advertisements, broadcast media campaigns, Internet communications, and seminars.

2. The salesperson can learn in detail about the prospect's needs and goals, discuss a variety of options with the prospect and tailor a policy to his circumstances, learn about any obstacles to paying premiums and suggest ways to overcome them, and uncover any potential underwriting problems.

3. Meeting with prospects one by one is very time-consuming, and an agent will often spend valuable time with people who have no interest in the product or who are not qualified prospects.

4. Cold calling is now subject to the Federal Trade Commission's "Do Not Call" rules, and even when it is allowed, it can be very time-consuming and can result in expensive telephone bills.

5. Proper targeting—making sure that those who receive the mailing are likely prospects.

6. Because the agent knows the people on her list, she can identify those who are likely to be interested and qualified and mail only to them, and because the recipients of the mailing know the agent, the response is likely to be fairly good. On the other hand, since the agent is sending material largely to people she already knows, the potential for uncovering new clients is limited. Also, an agent's pool of contacts is usually too small to generate a very large list.

7. The choice of publication.

8. In some areas the rates of local radio stations and cable television channels are low. An agent can also make use of broadcast media at no cost by appearing as a guest on a local program.

9. A marketing approach in which a knowledgeable sales professional makes a classroom-style presentation on a topic of interest to a group of prospects, with opportunities for one-on-one follow-up meetings in which selling can take place.

10. It enables agents to meet with a sizable number of people at the same time, get to know those people in a nonthreatening environment and establish rapport and trust, identify those who are qualified prospects, and obtain appointments for individual sales interviews. Seminar selling can also help build the professional reputation of an agent and company in a community and create marketing buzz about a product.

 8

Seminar Selling

» What You Will Gain from This Chapter

As a result of the reading, research, and thinking you do in this chapter, you will be able to explain the seven steps of a seminar selling campaign.

» The Seven Steps of Seminar Selling

There are seven steps involved in organizing and conducting a seminar selling campaign. They are:

- choosing an audience,
- attracting the audience,
- preparing the presentation,
- handling logistics,
- making the presentation,
- conducting a follow-up campaign, and
- preparing for one-on-one meetings.

In this chapter, we will examine each of these steps. During this discussion, an important point should be kept in mind: The purpose of a seminar is not to sell policies. It is to educate the public and obtain appointments for one-on-one, face-to-face meetings with prospects. Sales are made in these later meetings, which will be discussed in the chapter that follows.

» Step One: Choosing an Audience

There are several types of audiences for seminars. These include:

- a public audience, made up of anyone who learns about the seminar and registers for it;
- a preselected audience made up of invitees drawn from a self-generated list;
- a preselected audience made up of invitees drawn from a purchased list;
- a mixed preselected audience made up of invitees drawn from both a self-generated and a purchased list;
- a worksite audience, made up of employees of a sponsoring employer;
- an audience made up of members of a sponsoring association or organization; and
- an audience of other insurance salespersons.

Which of these should be chosen by a salesperson organizing a seminar? Each type has advantages and disadvantages, as we will see below. To some extent, the choice depends on the circumstances and preferences of the salesperson. For example, some agents and brokers like to concentrate on worksite seminars, others focus on fraternal organizations of which they are members, and still others enjoy working with a variety of audiences.

A Public Audience

A **public audience** is made up of anyone who registers in response to an announcement of a seminar (such as an ad in the local newspaper or a mailing). The members of such an audience are usually people the presenter does not know, and their circumstances and reasons for interest are diverse. For example, some attendees may be concerned about their own long-term care needs, while others are seeking information for older relatives.

A public audience gives a salesperson the opportunity to uncover new and unsuspected **client nests**. For example, an agent may meet and establish a relationship with a new senior client and as a result make a series of sales to three generations of prospects, including the senior's spouse, siblings, middle-aged children, and adult grandchildren. Or a new client might provide an entrée into his workplace or fraternal or service organization.

However, public audiences do present drawbacks:

■ It is difficult to predict the makeup of a public audience, so it can be hard to prepare a presentation that addresses the audience's concerns. For example, the audience may turn out to be much older or younger than the salesperson expected in preparing his talk.

■ Since a public audience usually consists of a variety of people with different concerns, it is hard to give a presentation that meets everyone's needs. For example, if the salesperson spends too much time talking to middle-aged attendees about the problems they face in caring for parents, older people in the audience may become bored or even offended.

■ Finally, some of those attending a public seminar will not be *qualified* prospects. Others may have already purchased long-term care insurance and be there simply to reassure themselves that they made the right decision.

An Audience from a Self-Generated List

A salesperson can create an audience for a seminar by sending invitations to a self-generated list of current clients, other people she knows, and referrals. This approach has a number of advantages:

■ The salesperson can invite only those likely to be qualified prospects.

■ The salesperson can invite people with similar concerns and focus her presentation on those concerns.

■ Because the salesperson knows a large number of those attending, her rapport with the audience should be good, and her comfort level in speaking before a group should be high. This can lead to a more effective presentation.

On the other hand, there are limitations to using a self-generated list to draw a seminar audience. Since only a small number of those invited will attend, to draw a large enough group may require a larger mailing list than an agent can generate. Even agents who have large pools of contacts are rarely able to fill one seminar after another for an extended period. In addition, because the seminar groups are made up of the salesperson's contacts, opportunities for uncovering new client nests are limited.

Research   Make a list of all the people you know whom you would invite to a seminar on long-term care and count the names.

Thinking   Consider how many of the people on your list would be likely to attend on any given date. If the number is less than 25, write down ways you could attract more people.

_____

_____

_____

_____

_____

_____

_____

_____

An Audience from a Purchased List

An audience can also be drawn by mailing invitations to a purchased list. This has certain advantages:

■ Since those on the list share certain characteristics, the agent can target her presentation.

■ Since those on the list are new to the agent, she may uncover new client nests.

However, there are also disadvantages to using a purchased list:

■ Because those receiving the invitations do not know the agent, there will likely be a lower rate of response than with a self-generated list. This means that more invitations must be sent to draw the same number of people.

■ Another consequence of the attendees not knowing the agent is that she will have to spend more time establishing her credentials and credibility and building rapport with them. This may lead to a longer sales cycle.

A Mixed Audience

An agent or broker can combine the use of a self-generated list and a purchased list. For example, when organizing a seminar for new prospects from a purchased list, an agent can also invite people she knows as a way of ensuring a minimum attendance level. There are other advantages to this approach—the agent can use the testimonials of long-time clients to establish credibility with new prospects, and the presence of people the agent knows adds to her comfort level in conducting the seminar. Alternatively, an agent creating an audience from a self-generated list who finds she does not have enough contacts can use a purchased list to bring in more people.

A salesperson combining the two types of lists should select people with similar circumstances and concerns from both lists. In this way a homogenous group can be created to which the salesperson can give a targeted message. Also, during the seminar, the agent needs to be careful about dividing her time between established clients and new prospects. The people she knows need to be acknowledged, while rapport needs to be established with new contacts. One veteran suggests having a spouse, close friend, or business associate available to meet, greet, and gather updated information from known faces while the presenter herself makes the new people feel welcome.

A Worksite Audience

Many employees view the workplace as an important source of information on topics such as retirement planning, health care options, and elder care solutions. And many employers seek inexpensive ways of providing employees with information that can solve personal problems that may affect attendance and the flow of work. In a **worksite seminar**, a salesperson presents such information to employees at their place of work, under the sponsorship of the employer.

How can an agent find employers interested in sponsoring a seminar? He should begin by contacting his current business clients as well as referrals received from them. He may also want to send a mailing to a list of employers.

Worksite seminars offer these advantages:

■ The time and location are very convenient for employees, so attendance is usually good.

■ The employer takes care of many practical matters, such as publicizing the seminar to employees, arranging for and setting up the room, and ordering refreshments.

■ It is easy to locate and contact attendees for follow-up appointments.

On the other hand, members of a worksite audience often have a variety of concerns, making a targeted presentation difficult. Also, many attendees may not be qualified prospects.

Research Make a list of business clients you could approach about sponsoring a worksite seminar.

Thinking Write down what you would say to persuade a businessperson to sponsor a seminar on long-term care planning and insurance for her employees.

_____

_____

_____

_____

_____

Other Sponsored Audiences

Professional associations, religious groups, and fraternal and service organizations may also sponsor seminars. As with worksite seminars, such an audience enables a salesperson to reach new clients without having to deal with such things as sending invitations, renting a space, etc. However, the salesperson should bear in mind the following:

■ Attendance is often poorer than at a seminar conducted at work.

■ The seminar may be part of a larger meeting and thus of limited interest to many of those attending.

■ As with a worksite seminar or a public seminar, concerns may be diverse and many attendees may not be qualified prospects.

■ The time allotted to the salesperson's presentation may be extremely short, so he may be able to offer only enough information to arouse the interest of some of his listeners and make them to want to learn more at a later opportunity.

An Audience of Other Salespersons

Long-term care is of interest to many insurance agents and brokers, and some of them must also fulfill requirements for continuing education credits. A seminar for salespersons can help meet both needs. A professional association may sponsor the seminar, or the presenter may send out invitations.

What does a salesperson gain by conducting such a seminar? It gives him an opportunity to network with other sales professionals and receive referrals. On the other hand, he may be training future competitors.

Someone interested in conducting seminars for other salespersons should be aware that having a seminar approved for continuing education credit requires a considerable amount of work. However, his home office may have seminar materials that are already approved for credit.

Audience Size

In addition to choosing a type of audience, a salesperson must decide how many people he wants in attendance. Of course, the larger the audience, the more potential prospects an agent can establish contact with. But if an audience is too large, it becomes difficult to meet personally with and learn more about each of the attendees. It is also difficult to contact all attendees and arrange for face-to-face meetings within a reasonable time after the seminar.

On the other hand, if a group is too small, different problems arise. Attendees may feel pressured by too much attention and fail to cooperate in providing information about themselves. Also, too small an audience may give attendees the impression that the seminar has failed, and this perception is likely to be reflected in their opinion of the presenter's professional abilities.

What is the ideal number of attendees? We believe 25. This is about as many people as a salesperson can meaningfully interact with during the seminar and meet with within a reasonable time afterward.

In trying to create a group of 25, a salesperson should keep in mind that last-minute cancellations do occur. She should shoot for 27 or 28 confirmed attendees in the expectation that two or three will not show up.

One Session or Several Sessions?

An agent might consider organizing not just one-time seminars but a series of two or three sessions with the same group. On the one hand, multiple sessions certainly add to the work involved, and attendance may be lower, since more of a time commitment is asked of attendees. On the other hand, multiple sessions can help cement the relationship between an agent and attendees, and more can be learned about their needs and objectives before private meetings are conducted, saving time in those meetings.

» Step Two: Attracting the Audience

Newspaper Advertising

How does a salesperson attract people to a public seminar? The most common way is by placing an advertisement in a local newspaper. Here are some are guidelines to follow in placing an ad:

- Place the ad in the business section of the paper. Readers of this section typically have the means to buy insurance and are more likely than the average person to be interested in a seminar on a financial topic.
- Do not place the ad in the classified section.
- Place the ad in the upper right hand corner of a page. Many sales professionals believe this is the best place for a seminar ad.
- Consider advertising in a weekend edition of the paper. Newspapers are typically more widely read on weekends.
- Do not purchase large blocks of advertising space. In most instances, a small, well-placed ad will be sufficient.

In drafting advertising copy, the following should be kept in mind:

- Focus on the benefits those who attend the seminar will gain. What will they learn? What will they receive? What problems will they be able to avoid or solve?
- Include your professional credentials and experience.
- Include contact information so that a reader who cannot attend but is interested in the product can reach you.
- Provide clear instructions on how to register.
- Note any cost.
- Ask your home office for advertising expertise. Some companies have an advertising kit that can be tailored to your specific situation.

Direct Mail

Another way to draw people to a public seminar is to blanket the local area with a mailing. However, direct mail is more commonly used to send invitations to people on a self-generated or purchased list.

A key question in using direct mail to attract seminar attendees is how far in advance to send the invitation. There are two contradictory approaches:

- **The early approach.** Invitations should be sent six to ten weeks before the seminar date. The thinking here is that people have many demands on their time and like to plan far ahead.

- **The late approach.** Invitations should be sent no more than five weeks beforehand. The reasoning here is that most people plan about this far ahead and if they receive a notice too much in advance they will put it aside and forget about it.

In deciding whether to send invitations early or late, the occupations and lifestyles of the invitees should be taken into account. For example, busy professionals often schedule their time far ahead, while retirees with lots of free time often do not.

Fee or Free?

Fees are another issue to be considered in attracting attendees. In the past, salespersons have generally offered seminars for free. Some sales professionals now recommend charging a small registration fee. They maintain that those who are willing to pay something in advance are more likely to attend and to have a serious interest in the topic. However, they may also have higher expectations in terms of the presenter's credentials, his presentation, and the handout materials they receive.

» Step Three: Preparing the Presentation

Of course, a salesperson cannot simply stand up in front of a seminar audience and talk about what she knows. She must organize the information she wants to share into a clear and appealing presentation. Some pointers:

- Create a script.
- Don't try to do too much. Focus on a few key points.
- Use visuals. Different individuals have different learning styles, and many people are visual learners.

■ Tell stories. Many people are best reached by real-life stories that illustrate problems and solutions.

■ Rehearse the script. This will make your presentation smooth and lessen any anxiety you may feel. It will also let you gauge how much time you are spending on each topic and on the entire presentation.

Some presenters use prepackaged seminar materials. These usually include a script and slides, and they are provided by some home offices and also offered by commercial services. Commercially produced materials should be reviewed for accuracy and approved by the presenter's carrier. An independent salesperson representing several carriers should make sure any materials he uses with the public have been filed with and approved by the state insurance department, if so required.

Handouts

A seminar presenter should prepare handouts for participants. These serve several purposes:

■ They provide information that attendees can take home and refer to later.
■ They inform the participants of the presenter's qualifications and experience. Thus they are an inexpensive and low-key form of advertising.
■ They show attendees that the presenter is well prepared and organized—the type of person with whom they like to do business.

In addition to informational handouts, the presenter should create an evaluation form. Participants will fill this out and return it at the end of the seminar. It provides feedback on the seminar and helps the presenter make improvements and better meet participants' needs.

Finally, there should be a questionnaire for participants in which they are asked to provide information about themselves. This information is important for follow-up contacts. The questionnaire can also include a written request for an appointment.

Any materials provided to the public should be approved by the salesperson's carrier and/or filed and approved by the state insurance department, where required.

Developing Expertise

Obviously, a salesperson leading a seminar should have an in-depth understanding of long-term care and long-term care insurance issues, not just enough knowledge to make the seminar presentation. He must be able to answer questions from the audience, some of them dealing with details and complications. If his command of the subject seems shallow, he will lose credibility, and attendees will go elsewhere for information and coverage.

Thus part of preparing for seminars is deepening one's knowledge of long-term care and related issues. One can do this by taking industry-sponsored courses, reading professional journals, and surfing the Internet. Salespeople should also become familiar with several local long-term care facilities and home health care agencies and learn about their services and costs. And agents should read the LTCI contracts issued by the carriers they represent.

In addition, it is a good idea for a salesperson to read articles about long-term care in the popular press. Not only will he discover information he can use in a seminar, he will also gain a sense of what the average person knows on the subject. This will help him create an easy-to-understand presentation and prepare him for the inaccurate ideas that many attendees will have.

» Step Four: Handling Logistics

The practicalities involved in organizing a seminar may be boring, but they are important. Poorly handled logistics can cause poor attendance, reflect badly on the professionalism and competence of the presenter, and make attendees frustrated and unreceptive to the presenter's message.

Some of the logistical issues are:

- the meeting place,
- the meeting time and date, and
- attendance confirmation.

The Meeting Place

In choosing the site of a seminar, the following questions should be asked:

■ Is the site conveniently located? Is it easy to get to by car or public transportation?

■ Is use of the site free, and if not, what is the charge?

■ Is there adequate parking? Is there a charge for it? How far is the parking area from the meeting site?

■ Is the site in an area considered safe?

■ Is the room big enough? Is it comfortable, clean, and pleasant? Does it have adequate seating and needed equipment, such as screens and easels for flipcharts? Are there facilities for refreshments?

Many potential meeting sites, such as public libraries and senior centers, may be available for free. Assisted living residences and other long-term care facilities are often happy to host a seminar and may even provide refreshments, especially if they have recently opened and are eager to attract potential residents.

Meeting Time and Date

The best time of day to hold a seminar depends on the target audience. For example, business people usually like to meet in the morning, before they are overwhelmed by work demands, while retirees often prefer the middle of the day, so they can avoid rush-hour traffic. Seminars given to religious groups and fraternal or service organizations may need to be scheduled at their regular meeting times. In setting times, allow for breaks. Breaks not only help attendees maintain their attention, they also allow the presenter to mingle.

In deciding on a date, popular vacation times and holiday seasons should be avoided, as well as major sporting events. In this regard, it should be remembered that attendees may come from diverse religious and ethnic backgrounds.

Attendance Confirmation

When someone registers for a seminar, he should receive confirmation that the seminar will in fact take place and that he is enrolled. Some sales professionals advise confirming twice: The attendee should be called or sent a postcard immediately after his registration is received, and he should also get a reminder call shortly before the seminar. Confirmation serves two purposes—it reminds attendees of the seminar and so boosts attendance, and it conveys professionalism.

Research

Look for a seminar site in your community. Check the Yellow Pages or advertisements in the local newspaper. Once you find a likely site, contact the person responsible for renting it and request information.

Thinking

After you have completed your research, write down the answers to these questions:

- Is the site near a highway or other major road?

_____

- Is the site close to public transportation?

_____

- Is there a rental charge?

_____

- Is there adequate parking? Is there a charge for it?

_____

- Is the area considered safe?

_____

- Are the facilities clean and pleasant?

_____

- Are there other features that make the site desirable?

_____

_____

_____

» Step Five: Making the Presentation

Pointers for delivering the presentation:

■ Dress appropriately. This can mean different things in different settings, but the bottom line is that you should look like a professional and your clothes and general appearance should not distract attention from your message.

■ Remember, don't try to do too much. Don't get distracted from the key points you have decided to focus on.

■ Use visuals to remind yourself of your key points and help you stay on track.

■ Don't get so bogged down in providing information that you forget to tell stories.

■ Let attendees know you are available to meet with them individually to discuss their needs. This should be done early in the presentation and at least once again before the end. Have someone available when the seminar concludes to schedule individual appointments for those interested.

■ Mingle with attendees before and after the presentation and during breaks. Get to know them and establish rapport.

■ Hand out evaluation forms and questionnaires at the end, ask attendees to fill them out, and collect them.

» Step Six: Following Up

As explained at the beginning of this chapter, the purpose of conducting a seminar is not to make sales. It is to obtain appointments for one-on-one meetings where sales can be made. A **follow-up campaign** is a coordinated effort to arrange such meetings with seminar attendees.

A follow-up campaign should include the following activities:

■ reading the questionnaires that attendees filled out and, based on the information provided, dividing attendees into groups of ready, possible, and unqualified prospects;

■ sending follow-up letters to attendees, both those who have expressed interest in a face-to-face meeting and those who have not;

■ sending follow-up e-mails; and

■ making follow-up telephone calls to obtain appointments and confirm those already requested. This can be a good time for the salesperson to request any additional information (such as health status) she feels she needs before the meeting. On the other hand, some salespeople prefer to wait until they have established a rapport with the prospect before they ask for such information.

Sales professionals generally agree that follow-up activities should be completed within two weeks after the seminar. This requires planning ahead. Before the seminar takes place, the salesperson should prepare follow-up letters, arrange for administrative help in sending letters and making calls, and put a contact management system in place to track personal interactions with attendees and mailings to them.

Some sales professionals suggest sending a periodic newsletter to attendees. Some agents are able to write their own newsletter. Others may want to purchase a professionally prepared newsletter on which the agent's name and contact information can be prominently printed. A newsletter allows the agent to stay in touch with attendees in a nonthreatening way, and it helps attendees remember the agent when they are ready to take action. Such newsletters should be reviewed and approved by the appropriate carrier and/or state insurance department, where required.

» Step Seven: Preparing for Appointments

To prepare for a one-on-one meeting with a prospect following a seminar, a salesperson should do the following:

■ Review what you know about the prospect. Reread her questionnaire and review the other information you have.

■ Consider what products and options are likely to be appropriate for her.

■ Review the underwriting guidelines of the company or companies you represent.

■ Decide whether you want to have the meeting in your office or the prospect's home. Having the prospect come to your office is less time-consuming for you, and it can set a more professional tone. On the other hand, visiting a prospect in her home may enable you to learn more about her and help you establish rapport.

» What's Next

In the next chapter, we will look at the face-to-face meeting with the prospect, and we will discuss how to make the sale and how to tailor a policy to her needs.

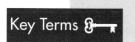

| Key Terms | Client nest | Public audience |
| | Follow-up campaign | Worksite seminar |

» Review Questions

1. What are the seven steps of seminar selling?

2. What is the purpose of the seminar itself in seminar selling?

3. What is the advantage of a public audience? What are the disadvantages?

4. What are the advantages of drawing an audience from a self-generated list?

5. What are the advantages and disadvantages of worksite seminars?

6. What is the advantage of seminars sponsored by associations and similar groups? What are the disadvantages?

7. How can a salesperson develop greater expertise in long-term care insurance?

8. What are some considerations in making the presentation?

9. What should a salesperson do to follow up with seminar attendees?

10. What should a salesperson do to prepare for an appointment with a seminar attendee?

» Answers

1. Choosing an audience, attracting the audience, preparing the presentation, handling logistics, making the presentation, conducting a follow-up campaign, and preparing for one-on-one meetings.

2. The purpose is not to sell policies, but to educate the public and obtain appointments for one-on-one, face-to-face meetings with prospects at which sales are made.

3. A public audience gives a salesperson the opportunity to uncover new and unsuspected client nests. The disadvantages: It is difficult to predict the makeup of a public audience, so it can be hard to prepare a presentation that addresses the audience's concerns; since a public audience usually consists of a variety of people with different concerns, it is hard to give a presentation that meets everyone's needs; and some of those attending a public seminar will not be qualified prospects.

4. The salesperson can invite only those likely to be qualified prospects, she can invite people with similar concerns and focus her presentation on those concerns, and because she knows a large number of those attending, her rapport and comfort level should be good.

5. Advantages: The time and location are very convenient for employees, so attendance is usually good; the employer takes care of many practical matters; and it is easy to locate and contact attendees for follow-up appointments. Disadvantages: members of a worksite audience often have a variety of concerns, making a targeted presentation difficult; many attendees may not be qualified prospects.

6. A salesperson can reach new clients without having to deal with such things as sending invitations, renting a space, etc. Disadvantages: Attendance is often poorer than at a seminar conducted at work, the

seminar may be part of a larger meeting and thus of limited interest to many of those attending, concerns may be diverse and many attendees may not be qualified prospects, and the time allotted to the salesperson's presentation may be extremely short.

7. Taking industry-sponsored courses, reading professional journals, surfing the Internet, becoming familiar with local long-term care facilities and home health care agencies and their services and costs, reading the LTCI contracts issued by the carriers the salesperson represents, and reading articles about long-term care in the popular press.

8. Dress appropriately, don't try to do too much, use visuals, tell stories, let attendees know you are available to meet with them individually, mingle with attendees, and hand out evaluation forms and questionnaires at the end.

9. Read and sort the questionnaires that attendees filled out, send follow-up letters and e-mails to attendees, and make follow-up telephone calls to obtain appointments and confirm those already requested.

10. Review what you know about the prospect, consider what products and options are likely to be appropriate for her, review underwriting guidelines, and decide whether you want to have the meeting in your office or the prospect's home.

9

Face-to-Face Selling

» What You Will Gain from This Chapter

As a result of the reading, research, and thinking you do in this chapter, you will be able to conduct a sales interview with someone who has expressed an interest in long-term care insurance.

» The Sales Interview

When someone expresses interest in long-term care insurance to a salesperson, either as a result of attending a seminar or for some other reason, the salesperson should arrange a **sales interview**. A sales interview is a face-to-face meeting in which the salesperson:

- explores the concerns that led to the prospect's interest,
- educates the prospect, and
- helps the prospect decide whether long-term care insurance is right for her.

Then, if the prospect decides she wants the coverage, the salesperson works with her to tailor a policy to her unique needs and circumstances and to complete the insurance application.

This chapter will examine these steps in the sales interview and explain how to execute them.

» Exploring the Prospect's Concerns

A salesperson should begin the sales interview by simply asking the prospect what concerns made him want to find out more about long-term care insurance. You should listen to what he has to say, and then, without getting into details at this point, explain briefly how long-term care insurance addresses those concerns.

Three general types of concerns are likely to come up:

■ **The prospect's memories of what happened to someone who needed long-term care and failed to plan for it.** Get the details. Ask what led to the person's need for long-term care, what it cost, and how she paid for it. Find out the impact this situation had on the person's family and on your prospect. Explain that long-term care insurance is an excellent way to plan ahead so that funds are available to pay for care when the need arises.

■ **The prospect's desire to age in place without being a burden to family or friends.** Ask why the prospect does not want to rely on family or friends. Ask if he knows anyone who has received care from a home health care agency, and ask how it worked out. Point out that long-term care insurance would allow the prospect to meet the costs of home care so that he could remain at home without relying heavily on family or friends. Add that it also covers assisted living and nursing home care should that become necessary.

■ **The prospect's fear that the cost of long-term care could wipe out family assets**, leaving his spouse destitute or making it impossible to provide for children. Ask if the prospect has seen this happen to someone else. If there are children with special needs (such as physical or mental handicaps or severe personal problems), find out what they are. Agree with the prospect that the costs of long-term care are high and getting higher and could deplete savings and income. Explain that LTCI benefits can help pay for long-term care, protecting assets and income.

Time spent finding out the facts and feelings behind a prospect's concerns is time well spent. It lays the foundation for the sale of a policy that meets the prospect's needs and makes him feel confident that he has adequately provided for the future.

» Educating the Prospect

At the beginning of the interview, your role is to ask questions, listen, and learn. Now you become an educator. You must teach the prospect about long-term care and long-term care insurance.

Using the information from the first half of this book, cover the following topics:

■ **What long-term care is.** Explain the difference between long-term care and acute care. Describe the activities of daily living (ADLs) and the instrumental activities of daily living (IADLs) and how they relate to the need for long-term care and long-term care insurance.

■ **Services and settings.** Describe the various types of long-term care and where and how they are provided.

■ **The likelihood of need.** Give some statistics illustrating how likely a person is to need long-term care sometime in her lifetime. Note that the probability of need increases as one gets older.

■ **Costs.** Give some figures on the current costs of various long-term care services and settings, and warn about inflation.

■ **Paying for care.** Review the other ways people may expect to pay for long-term care: savings and assets, family assistance, Medicare, Medicare supplement insurance, and Medicaid. Explain the limitations of each of these and the advantages of long-term care insurance.

As part of the education process, you may want to give your prospect a copy of AHIP's *Guide to Long-Term Care Insurance* (Appendix A), NAIC's *A Shopper's Guide to Long-Term Care Insurance* (Appendix B), and informational material from your carrier.

 **Research** You can print a copy of AHIP's *Guide to Long-Term Care Insurance* from the "Consumer Information" section of the web site (*www.ahip.org*). Or you can order copies

Research

through the Federal Citizen Information Center by calling 888-8PUEBLO (888-878-3256) (order item #331M, $1.00 each). Bulk orders of the guide are available to financial services and insurance professionals through the Life and Health Insurance Foundation for Education (LIFE) at *www.life-line.org/catalog* or by calling 800-268-7680.

You can get a copy of the NAIC publication *A Shopper's Guide to Long-Term Care Insurance* from your carrier, from the NAIC web site (*www.naic.org*), or by calling NAIC at 816-783-8300.

Research

Find out the range of costs in your area for the following types of long-term care:
- home health care,
- adult day centers,
- assisted living, and
- nursing home care.

You can get this information from your local Area Agency on Aging or Council on Aging. Or look up providers in the Yellow Pages and call them.

Fill in the table below with the data you collect.

Type of Service	Cost
Home health care:	
Skilled nursing care	_____ (per hour)
Physical, speech, and occupational therapy	_____ (per hour)
Home health aide services	_____ (per hour)
Adult day center care	_____ (per session)
Assisted living	_____ (per month)
Nursing home care	_____ (per month)

(For assisted living and nursing home care, note any ancillary charges.)

Write down how you would explain to a prospect the advantages of long-term care insurance over the other means of funding long-term care.

Thinking

_____

_____

_____

_____

_____

_____

_____

_____

_____

_____

_____

_____

_____

_____

_____

_____

_____

_____

» Helping the Prospect Decide

Once you have educated the prospect about long-term care, she must decide whether long-term care insurance is right for her. At this point in the interview, the NAIC _Shopper's Guide to Long-Term Care Insurance_ is particularly useful. In the section "Do You Need Long-Term Care Insurance?", there is a box titled "Is Long-Term Care Insurance Right for You?" It lists circumstances under which a person should not buy long-term care insurance and circumstances under which she should consider it. Go though these with the prospect.

» Tailoring the Policy

Fact Finding

If the prospect decides to buy long-term care insurance, you can begin the process of tailoring a policy that best meets his needs and circumstances. This process begins with **fact finding**—that is, obtaining from the prospect the information you need to help him make decisions on policy features and options and on the premium price. Normally, you will use a fact-finding form provided by your carrier to compile this information.

Financial Analysis

Using information from the fact-finding form, do a rough analysis of the prospect's finances to explore the possibility that he could pay for some of his long-term care costs himself, instead of relying entirely on insurance benefits. If he can, his insurance policy need not cover all costs, benefit amounts can be lower, and premiums can be less.

To make this analysis, answer these questions:

■ What is the prospect's annual income? Where does it come from (salary, Social Security benefits, annuity payouts, pensions, etc.)? Will any income sources end at a certain time (such as the salary of a prospect who is nearing retirement)?

■ What are his annual expenses (including basic living expenses, "extras" such as entertainment and vacations, debt payments, taxes, contributions to charities, special expenses such as providing for children with special needs)? Will any expenses end in the future (such as college costs or a debt that will be paid off)?

■ What is his annual **disposable income** (annual income minus annual expenses)? What will his future annual disposable income be (taking into account income and expenses that will end)?

To determine roughly how much of daily long-term care costs the prospect could pay out of his own pocket, divide his annual disposable income by 365. This is the prospect's income in excess of his expenses for one day. Make the same calculation for future disposable income.

You should also take into account the prospect's assets as a source of income to pay for care. Ask these questions:

- What is the total value of the prospect's assets? How much of this is in liquid assets, and how much is tied up in real estate and other illiquid investments?
- What are his total liabilities (such as a mortgage, a home equity loan, installment loans, credit card debts, or other debts)?
 - What is his **net worth** (total assets minus liabilities)?

If you determine that the prospect could pay some of the costs of care himself (from disposable income or assets or both), ask him if he would like to plan to do this and reduce his premium. Some prospects will be delighted at the possibility of a lower premium. Others will want to use future disposable income for other purposes and will be willing to pay a higher premium now to receive greater benefits later.

Although conducting a full fact-finding session is preferable, it is sometimes possible to appropriately structure an LTCI policy without obtaining all the financial details discussed above. If the client is financially sophisticated or has the guidance of a financial planner or accountant, the question may simply be, "If the need for long-term care arises in the future, how much money would you be willing and able to spend on it?" Based on the answers to a few more questions—"Would some of this money come from assets? What are those assets? Do you want to assume some of the financial risk of long-term care?"—the salesperson can choose some of the principal elements of a policy, such as the daily benefit amount and the elimination period.

> For practice, do an analysis of your own finances. Calculate your disposable income, excess income for one day, and net worth.

Thinking

_____

_____

Decisions on Features, Options, and the Premium

To tailor a policy to your prospect's needs and budget, discuss with her these questions:

■ **What services and settings does she want the policy to cover?** You should already have an idea of her preferences based on your discussion of her concerns. Go over the options available, and have her decide which ones she needs or wants. This could include any or all of them.

■ **What benefit amount does she want?** The amount should be based on the cost of the services the prospect has decided she wants covered. Also, as discussed above, you should help the prospect think through whether she wants the benefit amount to cover the entire cost of care or whether she will plan to pay for some of the cost from her own funds.

■ **How long a benefit period (or how large a maximum lifetime benefit) does she want?** As a general rule, a prospect should get the longest benefit period or the largest pool of money she can afford. If a long benefit period or large pool of money combined with a high benefit amount makes the premium too high, you should normally recommend shortening the benefit period or reducing the pool of money rather than lowering the benefit amount. The reasoning is this: If the benefit amount is inadequate, the insured will have to pay out of pocket every time she needs care. On the other hand, if she has a relatively short benefit period or small pool of money, she will have to pay only if she needs care for a long time.

■ **How long an elimination period does she prefer?** The longer the elimination period, the lower the premium. The prospect must ask herself both how long she can pay for her own care and how much she can afford as a premium. Someone with limited income may choose a long elimination period in order to keep her premium low, but in fact it may be easier for such a person to budget for a known premium amount than to have to pay a very large amount for care provided during a lengthy elimination period.

■ **Does she want inflation protection?** An inflation protection option ensures that benefits will rise to cover the cost of care in the future. However, inflation protection can add significantly to the price of the premium. Inflation protection is more important for a younger prospect (who, if she needs care, will probably need it years from now) than for an older person. A compound rate inflation option is more expensive, but it provides greater protection and may be needed by a young prospect. A simple rate option is cheaper and provides less protection, but it might be adequate for an older person.

■ **Does she want a nonforfeiture option?** This would allow her to derive some benefit from the policy even if at some point she decides to let it lapse, but it adds to the premium price. (With a tax-qualified plan, a nonforfeiture option must be offered.)

Once the prospect has made decisions on the above questions, the application can be completed.

Thinking

Tailor a policy to your own needs. Answer the questions in the preceding section and write down your answers.

_____

_____

_____

_____

_____

» Completing the Application

The prospect's answers to the questions on the insurance application are the richest source of information for the underwriting process. The application is also a legal document—it is the prospect's offer to enter into a contractual arrangement with the insurer, and the statements she attests to in the application become part of the insurance contract.

Because of the underwriting and legal functions of the application, you must ensure that it is fully and accurately completed in the prospect's presence and that she signs the document in all required places. Note that LTCI policies require more disclosures and signatures than many other forms of insurance.

After the prospect has signed the application, you must complete the agent's report and attach it. In this report, you explain to the insurer what you know about the prospect and provide any pertinent information not included in the application.

At the time of application, you are required by your state insurance department to provide the prospect with an **outline of coverage**. This is a very brief description of the policy's most important features. It has a standard format in each state so that prospects can use it to compare policies. You should also give the prospect a copy of the NAIC *Shopper's Guide to Long-term Care Insurance* and any Medicare guides required by your state.

Once the application has been completed, all required forms signed, and the outline of coverage and any other disclosures and receipts given to the prospect (now the applicant), you should take the time to make sure she is prepared for what will occur during the underwriting process.

- If a telephone or in-person interview is required (or possible on a random basis), tell her that she will to be contacted by the insurer or an insurer-appointed professional, and explain in general terms what she should expect during the interview.
- Let her know that the underwriting department might require copies of medical records and discuss how they will be obtained.
- Give her an estimate of how long the underwriting process takes on average.
- Tell her to call you at any time during the process if she has any concerns or questions.

Even if you discussed these issues earlier in the sales process, it is worthwhile to cover them again at the end of the application interview.

» What's Next

In the next chapter, we will examine the various tasks involved in delivering the policy to the new insured.

Key Terms		
Disposable income	Outline of coverage
Fact finding	Sales interview
Net worth	

» Review Questions

1. What happens in a sales interview?

2. Describe the three types of concerns that you are likely to uncover when asking a prospect why he is seeking information on long-term care insurance.

3. How can long-term care insurance address a prospect's concerns?

4. What are the advantages to a prospect of planning to pay some of the cost of long-term care from her own funds?

5. What should the benefit amount of a policy be based on?

6. How would you help a prospect decide on a benefit period?

7. How would you help a prospect decide on an elimination period?

8. What would you say to help a prospect decide whether to get inflation protection?

9. What would you say to help a prospect decide whether to add the nonforfeiture option?

10. Explain the importance of properly completing the insurance application.

» Answers

1. The salesperson explores the concerns that led to the prospect's interest, educates him, and helps him decide whether long-term care insurance is right for him. If the prospect decides he wants the coverage, the salesperson works with him to tailor a policy to his unique needs and circumstances and to complete the insurance application.

2. The prospect's memories of what happened to someone who needed long-term care and failed to plan for it, his desire to age in place without being a burden to family or friends, and his fear that the cost of long-term care could wipe out family assets.

3. It is an excellent way to plan ahead so that funds are available to pay for care when the need arises, it can enable the prospect to meet the costs of home care so that he could remain at home without relying heavily on family or friends, it covers assisted living and nursing home care should that become necessary, and it can help protect assets and income.

4. If she can do this, her insurance policy need not cover all costs, benefit amounts can be lower, and premiums can be less.

5. The cost of the services the prospect has decided she wants covered, and whether she wants the benefit amount to cover the entire cost of care.

6. As a general rule, a prospect should get the longest benefit period she can afford. If a long benefit period combined with a high benefit amount makes the premium too high, you should normally recommend shortening the benefit period rather than reducing the benefit amount.

7. The longer the elimination period, the lower the premium. The prospect must ask herself both how long she can pay for her own care and how much she can afford as a premium.

8. An inflation protection option ensures that benefits will rise to cover the cost of care in the future, but it can add significantly to the price of the premium. Inflation protection is more important for a younger prospect (who, if she needs care, will probably need it years from now) than for an older person.

9. This would allow her to derive some benefit from the policy even if at some point she decides to let it lapse, but it adds to the premium price.

10. It is the richest source of information for the underwriting process, and it is a legal document that forms part of the insurance contract.

10

Policy Delivery

» What You Will Gain from This Chapter

As a result of the reading, research, and thinking you do in this chapter, you will be able to prepare for and conduct a delivery interview with a new insured.

» Delivering the Policy

In the preceding chapter, we saw how a prospect decides to buy a long-term care insurance policy and submits an application to the insurer. Based on the application, as well as the salesperson's report, medical reports, and sometimes other information, the insurer makes an underwriting decision. If the insurer decides to offer coverage, and if the prospect agrees to any changes in the terms of the contract the insurer may require, the policy is sent to you, the salesperson. You then arrange to meet with the prospect to deliver the policy. In this meeting, called the **delivery interview**, you have several objectives:

- to confirm and reinforce the prospect's decision to buy the policy,
- to review the policy with him,
- to strengthen and confirm your professional relationship with him, and
- to set the stage for additional sales by discussing his other needs and by asking for referrals.

» Preparing for Delivery

Staying in Contact

While underwriting is taking place, call the prospect from time to time to let him know the status of his application. If there are delays, explain the reasons. Inform him of any changes that might be required and any additional information he may have to supply. In this way, you show that you are actively involved in the process and concerned about obtaining coverage for him. Also, this approach will prevent the applicant from being taken by surprise by any underwriting decision.

Checking the Policy

When you receive the policy, check it to make sure it is exactly the one applied for, and also make sure that the attached application (which becomes part of the insurance contract) is the correct one. Mistakes in issuing policies are rare, but they can happen. Key items to review are the services and settings covered, the benefit triggers, the benefit amount, the benefit period or pool of money, the elimination period, the premium amount, and any options the applicant has chosen. It is better to find mistakes before the delivery, as making corrections afterwards can be time-consuming and embarrassing.

If you discover an error, notify the company and send the policy back for correction. You should also tell the buyer that this has happened and that there will be a short delay in delivery of the policy.

Finally, in a few cases, an underwriting concern causes the insurer to issue a policy with a higher premium than the buyer expected. Understandably, the buyer may be upset, and the salesperson should be prepared to explain the reason for this change.

Anticipating Buyer's Remorse

During the finalization of any major purchase, it is common for the buyer to fear he has made a mistake. This phenomenon is known as **buyer's remorse**. The time to address buyer's remorse is during the delivery interview. If you do not deal with it then, even though the prospect may buy the policy, his misgivings may resurface months later and he may decide to let the policy lapse.

To prepare for the possibility of buyer's remorse, try to imagine the uneasiness the client may be feeling, keeping in mind the particular concerns and circumstances of the individual. Try to think of the questions the buyer may ask and be ready to answer them. Such questions will be along these lines:

- Did I do the right thing?
- Is this policy really the answer to my concerns and the best way to meet my needs?
- Can I afford it?
- Can I afford not to buy it?
- Can I get a better deal elsewhere?
- Is this the right time to buy, or should I wait?
- Can I count on help from the salesperson if I need it?

Thinking

Imagine you are about to deliver an LTCI policy to a particular client of yours. Think about the feelings this person might be having about his decision to buy. Below, write some of the questions that might be on his mind, leaving space for answers. You may want to use some of the questions listed above, but you should tailor them to the particular circumstances and concerns of the person you are thinking about, and you should add other questions specific to his situation. Then write what you would say to answer the questions in order to allay the client's worries.

_____

_____

_____

_____

_____

_____

_____

Setting Up Future Sales

Review the fact-finding form and your notes from meetings with the buyer, and identify any additional insurance or financial planning needs he may have. Also, search your notes and the form for the names of family, friends, and others mentioned by the buyer who might be potential prospects. You will need this information in the delivery interview to set the stage for additional sales.

» Conducting the Delivery Interview

Reinforcing the Buyer's Decision

When you meet with a buyer to deliver a policy, your first priority is to reassure her that she has made the right decision. You should begin by reminding her of her reasons for wanting long-term care coverage. You should also rekindle the feelings that led to a successful close. Congratulate the buyer on having made a wise decision that ensures that if she needs long-term care, she will be able to afford the services of her choice. Stress the peace of mind she will feel knowing that the insurance company will assume some or all of the financial burden of long-term care, a burden she was facing alone before she purchased the policy.

Reviewing the Policy

Most states require a salesperson to fully explain the entire insurance contract at delivery. And aside from legal requirements, it is in your interest to do so. By going through every clause and provision of the contract, you further educate the insured about how the features and benefits of the policy meet her long-term care needs. Also, by making sure the insured has a clear understanding of what is covered, under what conditions, and how much is paid, you can avoid misunderstandings and bad feelings later on.

You should begin your review by again reminding the client of the concerns that first led her to enquire about long-term care insurance. Next, talk about the decisions that you helped the client make as you tailored the policy to her needs. Then go over the policy provisions to show how they address those concerns, reflect those decisions, and meet those needs.

Be sure to cover the following:

- the disclosures on the cover page (most importantly the meaning of "guaranteed renewable" and the terms under which future premium rate increases can occur),
- the schedule of benefits,
- any excluded conditions,
- the definition of a provider of care, and
- procedures for filing a claim.

Most states require LTCI policies to have a **30-day free look provision**. This means that for 30 days after delivery, the new insured can return the policy for a full refund of all premiums and fees paid, even though the policy has already gone into effect. You must notify the insured of this provision and explain how it works.

During your review of the policy, listen for clues that the buyer might be concerned about something and address those concerns. If she seems satisfied at the end of the review, collect the first premium (assuming she did not have to submit it with the application).

If your client wants to reconsider the policy during the 30-day free look period, you may want to put her in touch with the health insurance assistance program in the state, which can provide well-informed guidance. To contact the program in your state, look up the telephone number in the "Directories" section of the NAIC's *A Shopper's Guide to Long-Term Care Insurance*. You may want to call them to find out what services they offer.

Securing the Salesperson-Client Relationship

One of your key objectives in the delivery interview is to strengthen your relationship with the client and secure your position as her insurance advisor. Remind the client that her new policy has been tailored to meet her specific needs. Explain that you will be conducting periodic reviews to determine if changes are needed. Warn her that if someone else recommends changing the policy or replacing it, it is important for her to let you know. Assure her that if she thinks a change may be needed, you will be happy to discuss it. Remind her you are only a phone call away and will gladly answer her questions and provide guidance to help her get the very best long-term care available under the provisions of the policy.

Pursuing Additional Sales

The close of the delivery interview is an excellent time to set the stage for additional sales. If you have done a thorough, professional job and met the client's needs, her positive feelings toward you should be strong.

During the initial discussion of concerns and the fact-finding process, you likely uncovered other insurance, retirement, or estate planning needs of the client. At this point, bring up the most pressing of those needs, and find out if the client is ready to take action. In some cases, the client will be willing to move forward immediately in other areas. If, on the other hand, the client is not yet ready to act, you can establish a date for the next contact.

You should also ask for referrals at this time. Go through the list of names of the client's family, friends, and other associates that you have gathered from your notes and the fact-finding form. Ask about each individual to find out if she is a potential prospect, and ask if you may use the client's name when contacting these people. (However, your contacts with these individuals must be in compliance with "Do Not Call" regulations.)

» What's Next

In the next chapter, we will look at the continuing contact between a salesperson and a client after the sale of a policy, focusing on how the agent can keep in touch with the client, be of service to him, build her relationship with him, and make additional sales.

Key Terms 🔑	Buyer's remorse	Thirty-day free look provision
	Delivery interview	

» Review Questions

1. What are a salesperson's objectives in a delivery interview?

2. What should a salesperson check before delivering a policy to an insured?

3. What is buyer's remorse? How can a salesperson prepare for it before the delivery interview?

4. How can a salesperson prepare for future sales before the delivery interview?

5. What are some of the ways a salesperson can reinforce a prospect's decision to buy?

6. Why is it important for a salesperson to fully explain an LTCI contract during policy delivery?

7. What two requirements do most states have in relation to the delivery of an LTCI policy?

8. How would you explain the 30-day free look provision to a new policyholder?

9. How can a salesperson secure the salesperson-client relationship during the delivery interview?

10. In what two ways should the salesperson try to set up future sales during the delivery interview?

» Answers

1. To confirm and reinforce the prospect's decision to buy the policy, review the policy with her, strengthen and confirm his professional relationship with her, and set the stage for additional sales by discussing her other needs and by asking for referrals.

2. He should make sure the policy is exactly the one applied for and the attached application is the correct one.

3. Buyer's remorse is the fear a buyer has during the finalization of a major purchase that he has made a mistake. The salesperson should try to imagine the uneasiness the client may be feeling (keeping in

mind his particular concerns and circumstances), try to think of the questions the buyer may ask, and be ready to answer them.

4. He should review the fact-finding form and his notes from meetings with the buyer and identify any additional insurance or financial planning needs. He should also search his notes and the form for the names of family, friends, and others who might be potential prospects.

5. He should remind her of her reasons for wanting long-term care coverage, rekindle the feelings that led to a successful close, congratulate her on having made a wise decision, and stress the peace of mind this decision will bring.

6. It is required in most states. Also, the salesperson can take this opportunity to continue to educate the insured about how the features and benefits of the policy meet her long-term care needs, and he can avoid later misunderstandings.

7. Most states require a salesperson to fully explain the entire insurance contract at delivery, and specifically to notify the insured of the 30-day free look provision and explain how it works.

8. For 30 days after delivery, the new insured can return the policy for a full refund of all premiums and fees paid, even though the policy has already gone into effect.

9. He should remind the client that her new policy has been tailored to meet her specific needs; explain that he will be conducting periodic reviews to determine if changes are needed; warn her that if someone else recommends changing the policy or replacing it, it is important for her to let him know; assure her that if she thinks a change may be needed, he will be happy to discuss it; and remind her that he will gladly answer her questions and provide guidance.

10. He should bring up other insurance, retirement, or estate planning needs, and he should ask for referrals.

Post-Sale Service

» What You Will Gain from This Chapter

As a result of the reading, research, and thinking you do in this chapter, you will be able to provide post-sale service to LTCI insureds in a way that builds a strong and mutually beneficial agent-client relationship.

» Keeping in Touch with Clients

After the sale and delivery of an LTCI policy, the objective of the salesperson is to turn the new insured into an established client—that is, someone who relies on the salesperson for guidance and solutions in the area of insurance and financial planning. A strong agent-client relationship benefits both parties—the agent makes additional sales, both to the client and to his friends and associates, and the client profits from the agent's expertise and assistance.

To build such a relationship, the agent's first step is simply keeping in touch with the client. By keeping in touch, the agent reminds the client that she is willing and able to be of service. And she also can learn more about the client's needs and suggest ways she can help him meet those needs.

A salesperson keeps in touch with clients primarily through mailings and telephone calls. A mailing should be sent or a call made on the following occasions:

■ A new product or option that might be of interest to a client is being introduced.

■ There are special opportunities, such as when an insurer offers its insureds new policies or improvements in existing policies for a limited period without medical underwriting.

■ Changes are made in laws, regulations, or government programs that may affect a client's financial planning needs. (These might include an adjustment in the limit on the tax deductibility of LTCI premiums or changes in the benefits, premiums, deductibles, or copayments of the Medicare program.)

In addition, a salesperson should periodically review a client's coverage to determine whether it meets his current needs. An offer to conduct such a review can be sent each year with birthday or holiday greetings. (The periodic review is discussed below.)

In some cases, a telephone call and a mailing can complement each other — for instance, an agent might call to let a client know that a brochure on a new product is being sent to him.

A salesperson should put in place some type of **client management system**. Such a system tracks contacts with clients and reminds the salesperson when a contact should be made. For example, an agent can set up her client management system to prompt her to call clients just after they have received their premium statements. Then, when she calls a client, she can ask him if he has received his statement and if he has any questions.

» Providing Service to Clients

Keeping in touch with a client is only the first step. A salesperson also wants to be of assistance to the client and help meet the client's needs as a way of building a relationship with him.

Maintaining Records

In order to efficiently provide continuing service to clients, a salesperson must organize the information she has on each client into a **client file**. She should include in this file the following:

- the fact-finding forms she completed with the client;
- a record of the decisions made by the client during the tailoring of the policy, along with the reasons for these decisions;
- a record of any recommendations she made that the client did not accept, along with his reasons;
- the rate quotes she showed the client;
- a copy of the application and cover letters to the underwriters;
- any notes she made on the client's needs and concerns or on possible referrals;
- copies of her correspondence with the client; and
- notes on any telephone conversations she had with the client or the client's family or other advisors. (These should include the date and time, the persons participating, and the content of the call.)

In addition, if a client's application is accepted but he decides not to take the policy, detailed notes on his reasons should be included in the file. (Some insurers even require a written statement from the client, signed and dated, declining the specifically named insurance policy.) Finally, if a client allows his policy to lapse, his reasons for doing so and any efforts on the part of the salesperson to maintain coverage should be documented.

The information in the client file serves a number of purposes. The salesperson uses it to review the client's coverage and discover any needed changes or updates. She also refers to it to remind her of any client needs that have been identified but not yet addressed. The client file also provides documentation if there are questions about the sale from the client, his family, the insurance company, the state insurance department, or the courts. The file should be maintained for the life of the client.

Answering Client Questions

One of the most basic ways a salesperson can provide service to a client is by simply answering his questions. Here are a few of the most common client questions:

- Is this expense covered by my policy?
- How do I find out what my benefits are under my policy?

- How do I file a claim?
- Whom do I contact if I have questions about a claim?
- How long is my premium grace period?
- How do I find out if the company received my premium?
- How do I change my mode of premium payment?
- How do I change my address?
- How do I get a duplicate of my policy?

In many cases, the best response to a question is to put the client in touch with the proper person or department in the insurance company.

Periodic Reviews

An agent should schedule **periodic reviews** with each of her clients. These are meetings held at regular intervals in which the agent and the client review the client's policy and discuss any needs or concerns. Periodic reviews enable the agent to make sure that the client's coverage changes to keep up with changes in his circumstances.

Specifically, in a periodic review an agent does the following:

- She goes over the policy with the client to see if he is still satisfied with the benefits it provides.
- She asks the client about any insurance or financial planning concerns or needs that may have arisen.
- She reminds the client of any concerns or needs that were left unresolved at their previous meeting.
- She suggests taking action to address at least one need.
- If action is taken, she completes the paperwork.

To prepare for a periodic review, an agent should go over the client's file. She should refresh her mind about the client's policy and his situation. For example, the agent may have uncovered several needs in the initial sales interview that have still not been met. Or she and the client may have agreed to future changes—they may have, for instance, planned to increase coverage after the client paid off his mortgage and could afford a higher premium.

Some agents send a checklist to clients several days before the periodic review. It asks questions about changes that may have occurred in the client's life and suggests some topics that the client may want to discuss. A checklist can speed up the process of finding and focusing on critical issues.

Thinking

List some of the changes that could have occurred in a client's life that should be discussed in a periodic review of his LTCI policy.

_____

_____

_____

_____

_____

_____

List some of the needs and concerns that a client might want to discuss in a periodic review of his LTCI policy.

_____

_____

_____

_____

_____

_____

» Providing Additional Products

We have seen that in the sales interview, the delivery interview, and the periodic review, the salesperson should not limit discussion to long-term care coverage but should explore all the insurance and financial planning needs of the client and offer to help meet those needs. What might those needs be? A client who has purchased an LTCI policy is someone who is concerned about providing for his future. There are a number of products that might interest such a person. We will focus on two of the most important, annuities and life insurance.

Annuities

As we learned in Chapter Three, an **annuity** is a type of investment in which the investor (the **annuitant**) pays money to an insurer or financial institution, and in return the insurer makes regular payments to the annuitant over a period of time.

There are different types of annuities based on how the amount of the payments to the annuitant is determined:

- A **fixed annuity** pays a fixed amount. Fixed annuities are appropriate for those who want a guaranteed income and minimal risk.

- In a **variable annuity**, the money paid by the annuitant is invested, and the amount of the payments made to him is based on the current value of the investments. Thus there is no guaranteed rate of return—the amount of payment may decline if the value of the underlying investments declines. On the other hand, if the investments perform well, the annuitant can earn considerably more than he would from a fixed annuity.

- An **equity-indexed annuity** combines features of the fixed annuity and the variable annuity. The amount of payments to the annuitant is partially based on a stock index (most commonly the S&P 500, which is based on the stock prices of 500 major companies). However, the annuitant is guaranteed a minimum rate of return. This type of annuity allows an investor to participate in the growth of the stock market while limiting his risk.

Annuities also differ according to how long the annuitant receives payments. A **life annuity** makes payments to the annuitant until his death. A **fixed period annuity** makes payments for a predetermined amount of time, regardless of when the annuitant dies. If the annuitant is still alive when this fixed period ends, he ceases to receive payments; if he dies before the fixed period ends, his beneficiary receives payments until it expires.

A life annuity provides financial security by giving the annuitant the guarantee that he will receive payments as long as he lives. However, a life annuity also carries a financial risk for the annuitant. The annuitant might die after receiving only a few payments or even a single payment. If this occurs, the annuitant will have received only a small part of the money he invested in the annuity. A fixed period annuity, on the other hand, offers protection against the loss of one's investment by guaranteeing that payments will be made for a certain time.

There are other variations:

- **A life income with period certain annuity** makes payments until the death of the annuitant, but in addition it makes payments for a certain amount of time even if the annuitant dies. In other words, if the annuitant dies before the period certain has elapsed, payments are made to his beneficiary until this period ends.

- **A joint life annuity** provides lifetime income for two people, usually spouses. It makes payments as long as one of the two is alive.

- **A survivor life annuity** is similar to a joint life annuity. It makes payments to the annuitant until he dies, and after his death it makes payments to his surviving spouse, although in some cases the amount may be reduced.

The amount of the periodic payment an annuitant receives in return for his investment depends in part on the financial risk borne by the insurer. For example, a pure life annuity makes somewhat larger payments than a life income with period certain annuity purchased for the same amount, because the insurer assumes less risk with the former than the latter—if the annuitant dies soon after purchase, with the former the insurer ceases payments but with the latter it continues to pay his beneficiary for a time.

Finally, annuities vary in how the annuitant purchases them—he may make one payment (a **single premium**) or a series of payments.

An annuity can be an excellent way to meet the needs of those planning for their retirement. For example:

■ For those concerned that their pensions, Social Security benefits, and other sources of income will not be sufficient to cover their retirement needs, an annuity can provide regular income.

■ For those concerned about outliving their savings, a life annuity can ensure income until death.

■ For those concerned about financial security, a fixed annuity can guarantee a minimum income level.

■ For those who want to increase their assets in order to have sufficient resources for retirement, a variable or equity-indexed annuity might be a vehicle for financial growth.

Annuities also offer tax advantages. The investment earnings of annuities are tax-deferred, and payments from annuities are partially tax-free.

An annuity can also be used to pay the premiums of an LTCI policy or for long-term care itself, as was discussed in Chapter Three.

A salesperson should keep in mind that clients who are not qualified prospects for traditional life insurance or LTCI products might be eligible for annuities since there is no health underwriting.

Research   Go to your primary carrier's web site and read the descriptions of its annuity products.

Thinking   After you have done your reading and research, write down what you would say to help an LTCI insured understand how one of your carrier's annuities could help guarantee him retirement income, build assets, defer taxes, or pay for long-term care insurance.

_____

_____

_____

_____

_____

_____

_____

_____

_____

_____

Life Insurance

As we have discussed, one of the main reasons people buy long-term care insurance is so that their accumulated assets will not be spent on care and can be kept intact for a surviving spouse or other heirs. People concerned about protecting an inheritance generally own life insurance, so almost all of those with an LTCI policy also have a life policy. Consequently, a salesperson working with a long-term care client rarely needs to sell him his first life insurance policy, but she can examine the life coverage he has to determine whether it still meets his needs.

There are two basic types of life insurance:

- **Permanent life insurance** (or **whole life insurance**) is designed to be in force for the entire lifetime of the insured. (It generally remains in force until the insured's death unless he lets it lapse by failing to pay premiums.)

- **Term life insurance** is in force for a limited period and pays a death benefit only if the insured dies during that period. It is appropriate for people who need a large amount of protection for a short time but do not wish to pay (or are unable to pay) for that amount of protection for life.

Over the years that a permanent life insurance policy is in force, it accumulates a **cash value**. This is an amount that the insured can draw on in various ways. For example, an insured may be able to borrow against the cash value of his policy. And when an insured retires, he may be able to convert the cash value of his policy into an annuity providing a lifetime income.

Thus a permanent life insurance policy may provide some retirement income. However, for most people the primary value of such a policy lies in the death benefit it pays after they die. They intend for this payment to be used to cover estate settlement costs and estate taxes, ensure adequate income for a surviving spouse or other dependents, and perhaps provide money for heirs and charities. Thus the death benefit of a life insurance policy is an important element in **estate planning**—making arrangements to protect one's estate and pass it on as one wishes.

Research Go to your primary carrier's web site and read the descriptions of its life insurance products.

Thinking After you have done your reading and research, write down what you would say to help a long-term care client understand how one of your carrier's life insurance policies can play a role in his estate planning.

_____

_____

_____

_____

_____

_____

_____

_____

_____

_____

» Educating Clients about Legal Documents

Another way a salesperson can be of service to a client who is planning for his retirement is to educate him about certain legal documents relevant to illness and the end of life. Of course, the client should consult with an attorney to learn more about these documents and have them drawn up, but the salesperson can bring the need for them to the client's attention. The salesperson can also help the client by providing a list of attorneys (but she should not choose an attorney for the client).

The legal documents in question are:

- a **will**, in which a person states what he wants done with his property after he dies;

- a **living will**, in which a person states whether he wants certain medical treatments and procedures to be used to keep him alive under certain conditions;

- a **power of attorney**, in which a person gives another person the authority to act on his behalf; and

- a **health care proxy**, in which a person gives another person the authority to make medical decisions for him if he is unable to do so.

Let's look briefly at each of these.

The Will

Nearly everyone knows what a will is, so a salesperson will rarely need to explain this to clients. But not everyone has a will, and not everyone's will is up-to-date, so she may need to persuade some clients of the importance of this document. In doing so, she should point out the following:

- If a person dies **intestate** (without a will), the courts of the state he lived in will decide how to divide his estate. Court decisions will be based on the state's **intestacy laws**, which may not reflect the wishes of the deceased. For example, a person may want all his assets to go to his surviving wife, but the intestacy laws of some states would give one-third to the wife and divide the other two-thirds among his children.

- The absence of a will adds to the cost of settling an estate. If there is no will naming an **executor** (a person who is given the responsibility of handling the estate, paying any debts, and distributing assets according to the will), a court must be petitioned to appoint an administrator, and this entails legal costs. And if there is no will clearly stating the wishes of the deceased, it is more likely that there will be disputes among heirs, leading to legal actions and legal fees.

■ The absence of a will may result in greater taxes on an estate. For example, in some cases federal or state laws allow a person to leave all property to a surviving spouse without paying estate taxes. But if in such a case the deceased has no will and the intestacy laws require that some of his property be given to other heirs, estate taxes might be levied.

The Living Will

As a general rule, it is considered the duty of a physician to preserve the life of a person under her care by whatever means are available. Consequently, a physician may at times take extraordinary measures to keep someone alive, or she may keep a patient alive whose quality of life many might consider intolerable. However, if a patient has a living will expressing how he would like to be treated in such a situation, in most jurisdictions his wishes must be obeyed.

In a living will, a person states what medical treatment he wants to receive or not receive in certain circumstances. If the person later becomes unable to make or communicate decisions about his medical care, the living will is presented to the attending physician. The physician must either comply with the instructions of the living will or have the patient transferred to the care of a doctor who will.

A salesperson should encourage her clients to make decisions about what treatments and procedures they would want under what conditions and ensure that those decisions are binding on medical personnel by making a living will. Many clients will feel they do not need a living will—they mistakenly believe this document is used only to instruct physicians to withhold life-prolonging treatment, whereas they might want such treatment. In fact, those who want to receive all available medical treatment in all circumstances should make a living will to make this wish binding on others.

The Power of Attorney and the Health Care Proxy

A power of attorney is a legal document by which one person (the **principal**) appoints another person (the **agent**) to handle his affairs while he is unavailable or otherwise unable to handle them himself. There are three main types of powers of attorney: general, special, and durable.

A **general power of attorney** is very broad and grants extensive powers to the agent. It might be used, for example, by an ill and homebound man to give his adult daughter the authority to write checks on his account when she buys things for him and to take other financial actions in dealing with his affairs.

The powers granted by a **special power of attorney** are limited to specified activities. For instance, a person might be granted a special power of attorney to complete a single real estate transaction or to handle only certain bank accounts.

A principal may grant a general or special power of attorney to an agent for a specified period or indefinitely. In either case, the principal can revoke the power of attorney at any time. In addition, these types of power of attorney ordinarily cease to be valid when the principal becomes mentally incapacitated. In other words, just when a power of attorney is most needed, when the principal is completely unable to make decisions, a general or special power of attorney may become invalid.

A **durable power of attorney**, on the other hand, does remain in force if the principal becomes mentally incapacitated. For this reason, it is advisable for some individuals to grant a durable power of attorney to a family member or a trusted friend. If this is not done and the individual becomes unable to make decisions about his affairs, his family will have go through the time-consuming and costly process of petitioning a court to appoint a guardian.

A health care proxy is a specialized power of attorney and is sometimes called a **durable power of attorney for health care**. In this document, the principal gives the agent the authority to make medical decisions for him if he is unable to make them himself.

A salesperson should explain to her clients how each of these powers of attorney works and encourage them to consider which they might need.

» Asking for Referrals

If a salesperson provides good continuing service to a client and builds a strong relationship with him, she will often be rewarded by selling him additional coverages and products. But she can also benefit by getting referrals from him and selling to his family, friends, and associates. In fact, asking established clients for referrals is essential to the success of a salesperson, as approaching people with a recommendation from someone they know is much more productive than prospecting among total strangers.

Therefore, a salesperson should make it a habit to ask for referrals every time she sees a client. When she sells a client a particular product, she should ask if he knows anyone else who might be interested. When she makes a service call, she should ask if the client knows anyone else who could benefit from the services she provides.

Many salespersons follow these steps in asking clients for referrals:

- At the end of a meeting, the salesperson asks how the client feels about the service she has provided.
- If the client expresses satisfaction, the salesperson thanks him and asks for his help. She explains (or reminds him) that her business grows through referrals from satisfied customers.
- She brings up people the client has mentioned in their meetings and asks for general information about them (such as age, marital status, children, place of residence, etc.).
- She asks the client to suggest other people he knows who might be interested in her products. She might ask the client to think of the one person he knows who would most benefit from these products.
- She asks the client for permission to use his name in contacting the people they have discussed.
- She asks the client for contact information for these people.
- She thanks the client for his help.

In contacting referrals, a salesperson must be familiar with and abide by the "Do Not Call" regulations mentioned in Chapter Seven. Her initial contact may have to be a letter introducing herself and inviting the referral to call her for more information. Or she could ask the person giving the referral to call or write his friend or associate, recommending the salesperson and providing her contact information.

» The Agent-Client Relationship

We conclude this chapter on continuing service to the client by offering a few final words on building a strong and mutually beneficial agent-client relationship.

Such a relationship is built on trust. The more a client sees an agent as a person he can trust, the more he will:

- seek the agent's advice and guidance,
- share information with her,
- accept her recommendations and act on them, and
- give her referrals.

Beyond trust, for a strong agent-client relationship to develop, the client must believe the following about the agent:

- She knows insurance and financial planning products.
- She understands me and my financial situation.
- She remembers what I say.
- She keeps in touch and is available when I need her.
- She is on my side and always has my interests at heart.

Finally, people want an agent who helps them think things through for themselves. An agent can best do this by giving a client options, helping him understand those options, making recommendations, and then letting him choose.

» What's Next

In the next chapter, we will focus on ethics in the sale of long-term care insurance. We will discuss the principles of ethical market conduct and look at voluntary codes of conduct and regulatory requirements.

Key Terms 🔑

Agent (of a power of attorney)
Annuitant
Annuity
Cash value
Client file
Client management system
Durable power of attorney
Durable power of attorney for health care
Estate planning
Equity-indexed annuity
Executor
Fixed annuity
Fixed period annuity
General power of attorney
Health care proxy
Intestacy laws
Intestate

Joint life annuity
Life annuity
Life income with period certain annuity
Living will
Periodic review
Permanent life insurance
Power of attorney
Principal (of a power of attorney)
Single premium
Special power of attorney
Survivor life annuity
Term life insurance
Variable annuity
Whole life insurance
Will

» Review Questions

1. After the sale and delivery of an LTCI policy, what is the objective of the salesperson?

2. What should be included in a client file?

3. What occurs in a periodic review?

4. Compare a fixed annuity and a variable annuity.

5. Compare a life annuity, fixed period annuity, and life income with period certain annuity.

6. How can some life insurance policies provide retirement income?

7. What role does a life insurance policy play in estate planning?

8. What are the disadvantages of not having a will?

9. How does a living will work?

10. Which legal document remains in force if the principal becomes mentally incapacitated, a general power of attorney, a special power of attorney, or a durable power of attorney?

» Answers

1. To turn the new insured into an established client.

2. Fact-finding forms, records of agent recommendations and client decisions, rate quotes, a copy of the application, notes on the client's needs and concerns and possible referrals, copies of correspondence, and notes on telephone conversations.

3. The agent and the client review the client's policy and discuss any needs or concerns.

4. A fixed annuity pays a fixed amount or a fixed rate of return. In a variable annuity, the money paid by the annuitant is invested, and the amount of each payment made to him is based on the current value of the investments.

5. A life annuity makes payments to the annuitant until his death. A fixed period annuity makes payments for a predetermined amount of time, regardless of when the annuitant dies. A life income with period certain annuity makes payments until the death of the annuitant, but in addition it makes payments for a certain amount of time even if the annuitant dies.

6. When an insured retires, he may be able to convert the cash value of his policy into an annuity providing a lifetime income.

7. The death benefit can be used to cover estate settlement costs and estate taxes, ensure adequate income for a surviving spouse or other dependents, and perhaps provide money for heirs and charities.

8. If a person dies without a will, the courts of the state he lived in will decide how to divide his estate based on the state's intestacy laws, which may not reflect his wishes; a court will have to be petitioned to appoint an administrator, adding to legal costs; it is more likely that there will be disputes among heirs, leading to legal actions and legal fees; and there may be greater taxes on the estate.

9. A person states what medical treatment he wants to receive or not receive in certain circumstances. If the person later becomes unable to make or communicate decisions about his medical care, the living will is presented to the attending physician. The physician must either comply with the instructions of the living will or have the patient transferred to the care of a doctor who will.

10. A durable power of attorney.

 12

Ethical Market Conduct

» What You Will Gain from This Chapter

As a result of the reading, research, and thinking you do in this chapter, you will be able to discuss the principles of ethical conduct in selling long-term care insurance and describe voluntary codes of conduct and regulatory requirements.

» The Principles of Ethical Market Conduct

An insurance salesperson or other professional involved in the marketing and sale of long-term care insurance must always conduct herself with honesty, integrity, fairness, and professionalism. In addition, she has other ethical obligations, discussed below.

Disclosure

An LTCI professional must disclose to her clients the information they need to make informed decisions. She must tell them about the disadvantages as well as the advantages of the products and services she recommends, and she must inform them of all costs. She should also disclose to them her own interest in any transaction. For instance, if she will receive a commission for the sale of an LTCI policy, she should let the purchaser know this.

Confidentiality

An LTCI professional must maintain the confidentiality of personal and financial information provided by a client. She may not share this information with others unless two conditions are met:

- The person receiving information needs it to perform a legitimate and appropriate business function (as when data is passed to an insurance company underwriter).

- The client gives his **informed consent** — that is, the salesperson explains to the client how the information he provides will be used, and the client agrees to this use. The client must give his consent in writing.

A salesperson must also make a reasonable effort to ensure that personal and financial information is not accidentally revealed to others. She should not leave applications, correspondence, and similar documents in open view, and she should take precautions to prevent sensitive conversations from being overheard. Finally, a salesperson must comply with all state and federal privacy regulations.

Competence

An LTCI professional has the responsibility to serve her clients with competence. Competence requires knowledge — a salesperson must be familiar with a broad range of LTCI products and have a thorough understanding of the features and provisions, the benefits and costs, and the advantages and disadvantages of each.

An LTCI professional must also have some knowledge of the other means of financing long-term care discussed in this book, and she should understand the implications long-term care insurance has for taxation, financial planning, and estate planning. But at the same time, she has an ethical obligation not to go beyond the bounds of her competence when advising clients. A salesperson who is not also an attorney, accountant, tax expert, financial advisor, or estate planner must always bear in mind her lack of expertise and credentials in these fields. While she can do her clients a service by alerting them to issues and concerns in related areas that they may want to explore, it would be inappropriate for her to offer specific advice in these areas.

Diligence

An LTCI professional must exercise diligence in serving her clients. She must take all reasonable steps to meet their needs and obtain necessary information and explore potential solutions.

Suitability

Finally, an LTCI professional has the obligation to recommend a product that is suitable for her client. **Suitability** means that the policy design, benefit amounts, selected options, and costs match the circumstances, needs, goals, and financial resources of the purchaser.

To ensure that a policy is suitable, a salesperson must exercise diligence and competence. She must make a systematic effort to obtain all pertinent information about a client's personal and financial situation and his concerns and goals. She must then use her knowledge of LTCI products and other approaches to find the best solution for the client. A salesperson must not simply get a general sense of a client's situation and recommend a product that "seems about right."

And of course, a salesperson must not knowingly and deliberately recommend a product that does not meet a client's needs. She must not sell long-term care insurance to a person for whom it is not appropriate, and she must not recommend a policy with more or fewer benefits than the purchaser needs.

She must also not engage in churning or twisting. **Churning** and **twisting** occur when a salesperson, simply to earn a commission, sells a new policy to someone who already has perfectly suitable coverage. (When the salesperson does this with one of her own clients, it is called churning; when she does it with the clients of other salespeople, it is called twisting.)

Write down what you would say to help someone understand how adherence to each of the principles discussed above protects the interests of consumers.

Thinking

_____

_____

_____

_____

_____

» Documenting Ethical Conduct

In the preceding chapter the documents, notes, and information that a salesperson should include in a client file were listed. If a client, his family, the insurance company, the state insurance department, or the courts question the salesperson's dealings with the client, or if a complaint or lawsuit is brought, the contents of the file can serve as evidence that the salesperson competently and diligently worked to provide the client with a suitable product, made all required disclosures, maintained the confidentiality of information, and otherwise adhered to ethical standards. If a salesperson is in doubt about what documents should be retained, she should consult with her carrier.

Research   Sales and insurer personnel: What are the guidelines and recommendations of your company in relation to the documentation of ethical market conduct?

» Codes of Conduct

Professional Codes of Conduct

The general principles of ethical market conduct discussed above have been formalized in professional codes of conduct, similar to those adhered to by attorneys, accountants, etc. The development of these codes has occurred as part of the trend toward certification of insurance and financial services professionals, and many professional designations (such as CLU, ChFC, RHU, CPCU, and CFP) have their own code of conduct that holders of the designation agree to abide by.

A good example of a professional code of conduct is the Code of Ethics and Professional Responsibility of the Certified Financial Planner Board of Standards. CERTIFIED FINANCIAL PLANNER™ certificants (CFPs) must adhere to these seven principles:

- Integrity—A CFP shall offer and provide professional services with integrity.

- Objectivity—A CFP shall be objective in providing professional services to clients.

- Competence—A CFP shall provide services to clients competently and maintain the necessary knowledge and skill to continue to do so in those areas in which he or she is engaged.

- Fairness—A CFP shall perform professional services in a manner that is fair and reasonable to clients, principals, partners, and employers, and shall disclose conflicts of interest in providing such services.

- Confidentiality—A CFP shall not disclose any confidential client information without the specific consent of the client, except in response to proper legal process, to defend against charges of wrongdoing, or in connection with a civil dispute with a client.

- Professionalism—A CFP's conduct in all matters shall reflect credit upon the profession.

- Diligence—A CFP shall act diligently in providing professional services.[1]

Visit the web site of the Certified Financial Planner Board of Standards (*www.cfp.net*) and read more about their Code of Ethics and Professional Responsibility.

An Insurer Code of Conduct: IMSA

In addition to the codes of conduct adhered to by individual professionals, there is a code that can be adopted by life insurance companies and their personnel and representatives. This is the Principles and Code of Ethical Market Conduct of the Insurance Marketplace Standards Association (IMSA).

IMSA promotes high ethical standards in the sale and service of individually sold life insurance policies, LTCI policies, and annuities. Life insurance companies that join IMSA agree to adopt and abide by IMSA's code. Specifically, an insurer commits itself to:

- conduct business according to high standards of honesty and fairness and to render that service to its customers which, in the same circumstances, it would demand for itself;
- provide competent and customer-focused sales and service;
- engage in active and fair competition;
- provide advertising and sales materials that are clear as to purpose and honest and fair as to content;
- provide for fair and expeditious handling of customer complaints and disputes; and
- maintain a system of supervision and review that is reasonably designed to achieve compliance with the IMSA Principles of Ethical Market Conduct.[2]

To become an IMSA member, an insurance company must show that its systems and programs to promote and maintain ethical behavior meet IMSA's standards. It does so by undergoing a self-assessment procedure and an assessment by an outside Qualified Independent Assessor focusing on the following areas:

- needs-based selling,
- legal and regulatory,
- policymaking,
- licensing and appointment,
- training,
- replacements,
- advertising and sales materials/illustrations,
- complaints,
- senior management's commitment to the principles and code, and
- supervision.[3]

To maintain IMSA membership, an insurer must repeat this review and assessment process every three years and demonstrate compliance with IMSA standards throughout the membership period.

 Visit the web site of IMSA (*www.imsaethics.org*) and read more about their Principles and Code of Ethical Market Conduct.

» The NAIC Models and Market Conduct

The codes of conduct we have discussed are voluntarily adhered to by professionals and companies. There are also laws and regulations governing market conduct that all those in the LTCI field must comply with. These vary from state to state, but as discussed in Chapter Six, the NAIC Long-Term Care Insurance Model Law and Model Regulation have been adopted, in whole or in part, by most states, so the provisions of these models apply in many parts of the country. Some of the provisions that relate to market conduct are the following:

■ A salesperson must give all prospects a shopper's guide to long-term care insurance. The NAIC has developed a shopper's guide that many states have adopted. It provides basic information on long-term care, long-term care insurance, Medicare, and Medicaid.

■ A salesperson must give a prospect an outline of coverage for the product she recommends. The outline of coverage must contain a description of the coverage; a statement of the principal exclusions, reductions, and limitations in the policy; a statement of the terms under which the policy can be continued or terminated; a description of the terms under which the policy may be returned and the premium refunded; and a brief description of the cost of care and benefits.

■ The application for insurance must be clear and understandable by the consumer.

■ The application must disclose the insurer's right to contest the policy if the applicant makes false statements on the application (see Chapter 13).

■ The policy must allow for a 30-day free look. As explained in Chapter 10, this means that during the first 30 days after the policy is issued, the insured may cancel the policy for any reason and receive a full refund of any premium he has paid.

■ The insurer must have procedures that ensure fair and accurate policy comparisons (to prevent churning and twisting) and prohibit the sale of excessive coverage.

Thinking 💡

Write down what you would say to help someone understand how each of the provisions of the NAIC models listed above protect the interests of consumers.

_____

_____

_____

_____

_____

_____

_____

_____

_____

_____

_____

» What's Next

In the next chapter, we will take a look at insurance company home office operations related to long-term care insurance. We will discuss the underwriting of applications for LTCI policies, the processing of claims on such policies, and ways of controlling claim costs.

Key Terms 🔑

Churning	Suitability
Informed consent	Twisting

» Review Questions

1. What two conditions must be met for a salesperson to disclose confidential client information?

2. To ensure that a policy is suitable, a salesperson must exercise _____ and_____.

3. Ted, an insurance agent, sells an LTCI policy to Will. But because of Will's limited income and assets, long-term care insurance is not appropriate for him. What principle of ethical market conduct has Ted violated?

4. What are some of the documents a salesperson should keep as evidence of her ethical market conduct?

5. What provision of the NAIC models is intended to prevent churning and twisting?

» Answers

1. The person receiving the information needs it to perform a legitimate and appropriate business function, and the client has given his informed, written consent.

2. Diligence and competence.

3. Suitability.

4. Fact-finding forms, due diligence checklists, copies of correspondence, and notes on conversations.

5. The provision that requires insurers to have procedures that ensure fair and accurate policy comparisons.

NOTES

1 Certified Financial Planner Board of Standards, Inc. 2003-2005. Code of Ethics and Professional Responsibility, pp. 6-7. Copyright © 2003-2005 by the Certified Financial Planner Board of Standards. All rights reserved. Used with permission.

2 Insurance Marketplace Standards Association. 2005. "Principles and Code of Ethical Market Conduct." *www.imsaethics.org*. Used with permission.

3 Ibid.

 **13**

Underwriting, Claims, and Cost Control

» What You Will Gain from This Chapter

As a result of the reading, research, and thinking you do in this chapter, you will be able to explain the basics of how long-term care applications are underwritten, how long-term care claims are processed, and how long-term care claim costs are controlled. (This chapter is an introduction to these topics, which will be covered in greater depth in the fourth book in this series.)

» Long-Term Care Underwriting

Underwriting is the process by which an insurance company decides whether it will accept an application for insurance and, in some cases, on what terms it will offer coverage to the applicant. This process consists of the following steps:

- A person submits an application for insurance coverage to an insurer.
- An underwriter employed by the insurer reviews the application and other information on the applicant.
- The underwriter decides whether the insurer should issue the coverage applied for, offer coverage under somewhat different terms (such as with a higher premium or a modification in coverage), or decline to offer coverage at all.

On what basis is this decision made? In essence, the underwriter tries to determine how likely the applicant is to make claims and then decides whether and on what terms the insurer is likely to receive enough in premiums from the applicant to recover claim payments made to him, cover operating costs, and leave a reasonable margin for profit and contingencies.

Underwriting Long-Term Care Applications

When LTCI policies were first introduced, underwriting decisions were based on criteria similar to those used in health and life insurance. That is, underwriters tried to determine the probability of claims by taking a broad look at the medical condition and history of the applicant. However, as insurers gained more experience with long-term care coverage and greater understanding of the risks involved, they came to realize that focusing solely on a person's current diagnoses and health history is not an adequate method of assessing his chances of needing long-term care in the future.

As a result, insurers developed new underwriting techniques that sharpened the focus on the probability an applicant will file a claim for long-term care services. Risk factors specific to future long-term care needs were identified, and in many cases these differed significantly from the medical conditions that indicate a high risk of needing medical care. The new underwriting techniques concentrate on the applicant's potential for cognitive impairment and the possibility that he will become unable to perform ADLs because of the gradual onset of a debilitating disease such as severe arthritis. These techniques include cognitive testing, assessment of the ability to perform everyday physical functions like ADLs, lifestyle review, and specialized medical review focusing on chronic degenerative conditions with a high risk for long-term care needs.

This shift in understanding of the conditions that pose a specific risk for long-term care was critical in improving the soundness of the LTCI product, as well as in expanding the pool of individuals who could potentially be approved for coverage. Based on the old, inappropriate "medical model" criteria, applicants were often unnecessarily denied coverage because they suffered from conditions common among the elderly such as diabetes, arthritis, cancer, or heart disease. Today, insurers look much more broadly at such conditions, taking into account their nature and severity and the physical functioning of the applicant, and they are able to accept many people with these conditions without affecting the integrity of the risk pool. Similarly, in the past applicants were often approved for coverage even though they had high risk factors for developing a costly cognitive impairment (or already suffered a cognitive loss) because the techniques to identify these factors at the time of underwriting had not yet been established.

Research

If you work for an insurance company offering long-term care products, find out the basic underwriting criteria and the common underwriting techniques used by your company for this coverage. If you are a salesperson, obtain this information for your principal carrier. Specifically, find out what conditions automatically exclude someone from obtaining coverage and what conditions constitute cause for further investigation before an underwriting decision can be made. Learn which common medical conditions are *not* a factor in underwriting for long-term care insurance but are important in health or life insurance.

» Processing Long-Term Care Claims

When a long-term care insured submits a claim to an insurance company, it must be determined whether the claim is valid under the terms of the policy. It is important that an insurer pay only those claims that are valid — if an insurer pays many invalid claims, there may not be enough money from insureds' premiums to cover valid claims, creating the potential for premium rate increases and making long-term care insurance affordable to fewer people.

To confirm the validity of a claim and to determine other matters related to the claim, insurers establish claim-processing procedures. The following five steps show how these procedures might be structured:

- Step One: Is the claimant covered?
- Step Two: Is the policy contestable or incontestable?
- Step Three: Is the loss covered?

- Step Four: What benefit options has the insured chosen?
- Step Five: To whom should the benefit be paid?

Step One: Is the Claimant Covered?

The first step in processing a long-term care claim is verifying that the person making the claim is in fact covered by a policy issued by the insurer. Claims are often submitted by a family member or care provider on behalf of an insured, so inadvertent errors do occur. For instance, someone making a claim for a relative may misunderstand the name of the person's insurer or may not know that the person no longer has long-term care coverage. Or a provider submitting a claim for a patient may confuse two patients with similar names or the same medical condition.

Once the claim examiner has confirmed that the claimant has a valid policy with the insurer, he must verify that the policy was in force at the time of the claimed loss. To determine this, the claim examiner first notes the date the policy was issued. Next, he ascertains the date or dates of the loss—that is, the dates on which the services for which the insured is claiming benefits were rendered. He then confirms that the policy was issued before the claimed services were provided.

The claim examiner must also review records of premium payments to verify that the insured had not stopped paying premiums and allowed the policy to lapse at the time of the loss. It should be noted, however, that a policy is still considered in force during the **premium grace period**. This is a period (typically 65 days after the date the premium is due) during which, even if the insured has not paid the premium, coverage is not discontinued. (State laws vary in regard to exactly how this "grace period" must be administered.)

Some insureds submit the first claim after care has already begun to be provided, while others notify the insurer of their desire to start receiving care and benefits. For example, an individual who suffers a stroke begins to receive medical and personal care immediately and submits a claim later. On the other hand, a person may be cared for by a family member for a time but slowly develop the need for professional care, in which case she may notify her insurer of this need and her intent to begin filing claims.

Step Two: Is the Policy Contestable or Incontestable?

Consider the following case: On an application for insurance, a person omits information that is material to the underwriting decision. Specifically, the applicant does not mention a medication he is taking and a diagnosis he has received at the time he applies. In reliance on the statements in the application, the insurer issues coverage. Later, after the policy is in force, the insurer discovers the applicant's misrepresentation. In such a case, claims may be invalid, and the insurer may even be allowed to rescind the policy.

However, many LTCI policies include an **incontestable clause**. This clause states that, after the policy has been in force for a certain period (usually two years), coverage cannot be denied because of any misstatements in the application (unless a deliberate intent to defraud can be proven, which is usually difficult to do).

The initial two-year period during which the insurer may deny coverage on the grounds of false or omitted information on the application is known as the **contestable period**. During this period, it does not matter if the pertinent statement, answer, or omission was intentional or unintentional, as long as it is material to the insurer's evaluation of the application when it was originally submitted.

How does the incontestable clause affect the processing of a claim? A claim examiner should note whether the policy under which a claim is filed is contestable or incontestable. If the policy is still in the contestable period, the claim examiner should be particularly alert to indications of misrepresentation, omission, or fraud on the application. This is especially true if a claim is filed very early in the life of a policy.

Step Three: Is the Loss Covered?

The next step in the claim process is verifying that the insured's loss (that is, the expenditure incurred for long-term care services) is covered by the policy. The following must be considered:

- **Benefit triggers.** As we learned in Chapter Six, certain conditions (called benefit triggers) must be met for long-term care benefits to be paid. Benefit triggers vary somewhat from policy to policy, but typically benefits are triggered when an insured is unable to perform a certain number of specified ADLs, or when she has a cognitive impairment. The claim examiner must verify that benefit triggers have been met by examining information on the nature and degree of the insured's inability to perform the ADLs or her cognitive loss. This information is usually obtained from the insurer's in-person assessment of the insured, medical records, or both. If the claimant has submitted previous claims for the same condition or services, the claim examiner should determine whether the claimant's condition has improved to the extent that benefit triggers are no longer satisfied. This is done by reviewing information available from the claimant's care coordinator or another provider familiar with her care. It should be kept in mind that because the eligibility of long-term care claims depends on the inability to perform ADLs or the need for supervision because of a cognitive impairment, medical records or information from the claimant's physician, traditionally used to manage medical and disability claims, are often irrelevant.

- **The cause of the loss.** The insured's need for long-term care services must result from a cause covered by the policy. Policies may exclude certain causes, such as alcoholism, drug addiction, or intentionally self-inflicted wounds. In addition, some policies exclude losses resulting from a **preexisting condition** (a medical condition the insured had before her policy went into effect). However, this exclusion typically applies only to losses incurred during the first six months of coverage; after that time, a loss resulting from a preexisting condition is covered. Moreover, today most LTCI policies do not exclude preexisting conditions. (One exception is employer-sponsored plans offered without underwriting or with limited underwriting.)

- **The types of services claimed.** As we have seen, many LTCI policies cover only certain types of services. For example, a policy may pay benefits only for nursing home care, in which case a claim for home health care services would not be eligible. The language of a policy is generally very specific in describing the services, providers, and facilities that are and are not covered.

■ **Provider licenses and certifications and other requirements.** LTCI policies generally stipulate that service providers and facilities must be properly licensed or certified for care received from them to be covered. For example, physical therapy may be a covered service under a particular policy, but if it is provided by someone who is not a licensed physical therapist, the claim would not be eligible. Documentation of licensure or certification should be obtained by the insurer when a claim is evaluated. A policy is also likely to stipulate additional criteria that a provider or facility must satisfy (such as staffing ratios, maintenance of medical records, etc.). For providers or facilities not subject to state licensure requirements (such as independent home care providers), the policy language will specify what criteria are considered equivalent to having a license.

To determine whether benefit triggers have occurred, what services were provided, etc., and to obtain other information needed to verify a claim, a claim examiner needs certain documentation. The documentation required depends on whether a first-time claim or a subsequent claim for the same condition or services is being processed—more documentation is generally required for first-time claims.

A first-time claim must normally be accompanied by a completed claim form, in which the basic facts of the case are reported, and a **certification by a licensed health care practitioner** (a physician or nurse). A certification is a written statement describing the nature and degree of the insured's physical or cognitive loss, the services she requires, and how often and how long those services may be needed. The licensed health care practitioner generally bases his certification on an objective in-person assessment of the insured, although sometimes he is able to make an evaluation based solely on a precipitating medical event (such as a stroke).

A policy will stipulate whether the certification can be from any licensed health care practitioner or only from one designated by the insurer. Practitioners chosen by insurers to perform long-term care assessments are usually specially trained in this area and so are better able to fairly evaluate needs than the average physician or nurse. And for the insured, an advantage of obtaining certification from the insurer's practitioner is that the cost is paid by the insurer.

Both first-time and subsequent claims must be accompanied by itemized bills from providers specifying the services rendered and the dates of service. Over the life of a claim (which may be months or years, depending on the severity and permanence of the insured's condition), it is necessary to regularly review objective information that documents the claimant's care needs. This information may be obtained from a variety of sources, including the claimant's care coordinator, care providers, or personal physician.

Step Four: What Benefit Options Has the Insured Chosen?

Whether a benefit is paid for a claim and how much is paid depend on three options chosen by the insured when she purchased the policy:

- **The elimination period.** A policy's elimination period must be satisfied before benefits are paid. For example, Joe Parker is unable to perform two ADLs, and so under the terms of his policy he is eligible for benefits. However, his policy has a 90-day elimination period. Depending on the specific language of the policy, this may mean that Joe must incur expenses covered under the policy and pay them himself for 90 days, after which, provided he is still eligible for benefits, the insurer will begin to pay. Alternatively, under some policies, it means only that Joe must remain ADL-impaired for 90 days, whether he incurs expenses for covered services or not (with perhaps family members providing care). If Joe must incur eligible expenses for 90 days, under most policies these do not have to be consecutive days—that is, he may satisfy the elimination period by receiving services on 90 days over, for instance, a 180-day period. This is an important provision, as many people receiving long-term care do not need services every day.

- **The benefit period or maximum benefit amount.** Once the total amount of benefits payable by a policy has been paid, the insured receives no additional benefits. For example, the benefit period of William Barker's policy is three years. William has now received benefits for exactly three years, so no more benefits can be paid. Another example: Laura Castle has a policy with a maximum benefit of $150,000. She has been in a nursing home costing $100 per day for just over four years and during that time she has received exactly $150,000 in benefit payments. So in her case too, no more benefits can be paid.

■ **The daily (or monthly) benefit amount.** Under most policies, the dollar amount paid on a claim is the lesser of these two amounts: the amount charged by the provider for services, or the benefit amount chosen by the insured when she bought the policy. In other words, actual provider charges are paid up to the policy's benefit amount, which serves as an upper limit on benefit payments. However, some policies pay benefits on an indemnity basis—that is, they pay the benefit amount chosen when the policy was purchased, even if actual expenses are less. In addition, some policies have different benefit amounts for different settings and services. Typically, the benefit amount for home health care services is defined as a percentage of the benefit amount for nursing home care. (The purchaser may usually select from a range of percentages, often 50, 75, 80, or 100 percent.)

Step Five: To Whom Should the Benefit Be Paid?

The final step in processing a long-term care claim is determining where to send the benefit payment (or in some cases the notification that the claim is denied). There are two possibilities:

■ In most cases the insured pays the provider for services out of her own pocket and then submits a claim to the insurer for reimbursement. When this occurs, the insurer issues the check to the insured.

■ In other cases the insured assigns benefits to the provider. Under **assignment of benefits**, instead of paying the provider herself and seeking reimbursement from her insurer, the insured authorizes the insurer to pay the provider directly. The provider submits the claim to the insurer, and the insurer sends the benefit payment to the provider. The insurer also usually sends the insured information about the benefits paid (called an **explanation of benefits**). The insured is encouraged to review the explanation of benefits to verify that it accurately reflects the services she received and their cost.

While assignment of benefits is very common in health insurance claims, they are an exception in long-term care claims. This is because most long-term care facilities and many home health care providers require that patients pay them directly.

The claim process described above is typical. However, each company has its own claim procedures. Find out the basic procedures for your company or principal carrier and compare them to the steps listed above.

» Controlling Claim Costs

The long-term care insurance field is faced with a challenge. Insurers must strike a balance between providing coverage that is comprehensive enough to meet people's needs and keeping premiums affordable so that long-term care insurance is available to a broad population. Insurers are working to meet this challenge by controlling costs, including claim costs.

An insurer's claim costs are affected by how underwriting is conducted, how claims are processed, and how care is managed. In this section we will look at four aspects of claim costs:

- incidence,
- intensity,
- duration, and
- unit cost.

Incidence

Incidence is the frequency of claims. A long-term care underwriter can reduce incidence by identifying applicants who are very likely to submit numerous claims in the near future. She should carefully review every applicant's health status, paying particular attention to medical conditions that can lead to physical or cognitive impairment. Claim personnel can reduce incidence by following the procedures described in the previous section to ensure that only valid claims are paid.

Intensity

Intensity refers to the type, cost, and frequency of the services that are provided. For example, a claimant might need physical therapy, which must be conducted by a licensed therapist, or she might need a less costly type of care, such as help with bathing and dressing, which can be provided by a lower-paid home health care aide. The frequency of services is often a function of the degree of impairment—a person who needs help with only two ADLs (most often bathing and dressing) may need someone to come in only once or twice a day, but an individual who also requires help with toileting needs someone most of the day. Family assistance is also a factor—a person whose family can help care for her does not need as much paid care as someone who lives alone.

The intensity of claims can be reduced by taking steps to see that each insured receives the level of care appropriate to her needs, while avoiding unnecessary services. There are several strategies for achieving this:

- **care planning**—assessing the insured's care needs and planning how best to meet those needs;

- **ongoing care coordination**—monitoring the care being provided by reviewing invoices, itemized bills, and caregiver notes; conducting periodic reviews of the insured's needs; and, where appropriate, suggesting changes in the way those needs are met;

- **informal caregiver support**—helping family members and other concerned nonprofessionals meet at least some of an insured's long-term care needs if they so desire;

- **community-based care**—encouraging the use of community-based services, such as adult day centers; and

- **resource coordination**—making sure an insured, in addition to her LTCI benefits, is receiving all other available assistance (such as from government and community programs, which may offer free or low-cost alternatives).

As mentioned earlier, many policies have limited lifetime benefits. Good claims practices like those listed above, when followed consistently and in cooperation with the claimant and her family, can help ensure that available benefits are used wisely and last as long as possible.

Duration

Duration refers to the length of time services are provided. For example, two claims might be for the same level of care, skilled nursing care, but one claimant might need to stay in a nursing home for only a few months to receive rehabilitative care for an injury, while another claimant must remain in such a facility indefinitely because of a serious and permanent impairment in functioning.

Efforts to control costs by controlling the duration of claims involve periodic reviews of each claimant's case to verify that the services being provided are still needed. The frequency of these reviews varies according to the nature and degree of the impairment and the expectations for recovery or further loss. For instance, to return to the example in the preceding paragraph, the claimant receiving nursing home care for a condition expected to improve should be monitored more frequently than the claimant with the permanent impairment.

Unit Cost

Unit cost is the amount paid for a specific service. This amount is not always the same—two insureds receiving the same services may submit claims for different amounts because different providers charge differently. For example, John and Steve both receive home health aide visits three times a week, but John pays $10 more per visit and so submits larger claims to his insurer. Of course, costs differ according to geographic location, but they also vary within a locality.

Efforts to control unit costs generally focus on influencing provider charges. An insurer might negotiate charges with a provider, or it might establish a network of providers that agree to provide services at a certain price or offer a discount to insureds. In addition, some insurers try to lower unit cost by employing care coordinators who can help an insured find an equally qualified but lower-cost provider for a particular service.

Write down how you would explain the aspects of claim costs discussed above and the cost-control measures associated with each.

_____

_____

_____

_____

_____

_____

Thinking

_____

_____

_____

_____

_____

_____

» Broad Factors in Claim Costs

In the previous section, we saw how an insurer's underwriting, claim processing, and management of care can help control claim costs. However, the amount a company pays in long-term care claims is also influenced by broader factors, including the types of LTCI policies the company sells and the market it sells to.

Comprehensive vs. Facility-Care-Only Policies

Some long-term care insurers offer policies that cover only care provided in a facility (such as a nursing home or assisted living residence) as well as policies that cover services provided both in facilities and in other settings. In general, a policy with fewer benefits has less risk of higher-than-expected claim levels, so that companies offering more comprehensive policies generally run a greater risk for the cost of claims. On the other hand, a policy with more comprehensive benefits is likely to attract more applicants, and this could lead to a larger pool of insureds and reduce the risk of **adverse selection**. (Adverse selection occurs when the population of those who apply for coverage includes a disproportionately large number of people who are very likely to need benefits.)

Characteristics of the Client Base

As we have seen, the older a person is, the more likely he is to need long-term care services. Therefore, a company that focuses its long-term care marketing efforts on older people will have high claim levels. Married people tend to use fewer long-term care services than single people, because they can care for each other. Women tend to use more long-term care services than men, because they outlive men and so are more likely to be single when they need care. Consequently, a client population that includes more single people and females is likely to have higher claim levels than one with more married people and males. Therefore, insurers must consider the age, marital status, and gender of the consumers they are selling to in estimating the claim levels they need to price for.

The Location of the Client Base

Because prices of long-term care services vary from place to place, the geographic location of a company's insureds has an impact on its claim costs. However, it is not necessarily the case that in some locations costs are uniformly high and in other places all costs are low. For example, nursing homes tend to charge less in rural areas, but in some of these areas there is a lack of home health care workers, so that people who could be cared for at home are forced to enter nursing homes, at a greater cost to their insurers.

It should also be kept in mind that where people are living when they purchase coverage may not be where they will be living when they receive care. A person in a high-cost area may retire to a low-cost area, or someone in a low-cost area may move to a high-cost area to be close to family members.

» What's Next

You have reached the end of this book. If you have done your reading, research, and thinking in each chapter, you have developed an understanding of what long-term care is, what options exist for meeting long-term care needs, why long-term care insurance is the best option for many people, and how long-term care insurance can be brought to those who need it.

What you have learned in this book lays a foundation for further study. The subsequent books in this series will build on this foundation and expand your knowledge of this field.

Key Terms 🔑

Adverse selection	Incontestable clause
Assignment of benefits	Informal caregiver support
Care planning	Intensity
Certification by a licensed health care practitioner	Ongoing care coordination
Community-based care	Preexisting condition
Contestable period	Premium grace period
Duration	Resource coordination
Explanation of benefits	Underwriting
Incidence	Unit cost

» Review Questions

1. How does long-term care underwriting differ from underwriting for other health insurance coverages?

2. What is a premium grace period?

3. What is the contestable period, and how long does it usually last?

4. What must be considered in determining if a claimed loss is covered by an LTCI policy?

5. What documentation must usually be provided with a long-term care claim?

6. What benefit options chosen by the insured affect the payment of benefits?

7. What is meant by incidence of claims?

8. What is meant by intensity of claims?

9. What is meant by duration of claims?

10. What is meant by unit cost of claims?

» Answers

1. Instead of taking a broad look at the medical condition and history of the applicant, LTCI underwriters concentrate on the applicant's potential for cognitive impairment and the possibility that he will become unable to perform ADLs because of the gradual onset of a debilitating disease such as severe arthritis.

2. It is a period (typically 65 days after the date the premium is due) during which, even if the insured has not paid the premium, coverage is not discontinued.

3. It is the initial period during which the insurer may deny coverage on the grounds of false or omitted information on the application; it usually lasts two years.

4. Benefit triggers, the cause of the loss, the types of services claimed, and provider licenses and certifications and other requirements.

5. A first-time claim must normally be accompanied by a completed claim form, in which the basic facts of the case are reported, and a certification by a licensed health care practitioner. Both first-time and subsequent claims must be accompanied by itemized bills from providers specifying the services rendered and the dates of service.

6. The elimination period, the benefit period or maximum benefit amount, and the daily (or monthly) benefit amount.

7. The frequency of claims.

8. The type, cost, and frequency of the services that are provided.

9. The length of time services are provided.

10. The amount paid for a specific service.

Guide to Long-Term Care Insurance
America's Health Insurance Plans (AHIP)

» Contents

» What Is Long-Term Care?

Insurance is an important tool for protecting yourself against risk. For instance, health insurance pays your doctor and hospital bills if you get sick or injured. But how can you help protect yourself against the significant financial risk posed by the potential need for long-term care services, either in a nursing home or in your own home?

Long-term care goes beyond medical care and nursing care to include all the assistance you could need if you ever have a chronic illness or disability that leaves you unable to care for yourself for an extended period of time. You can receive long-term care in a nursing home, assisted-living facility, or in your own home. Though older people use the most long-term care services, a young or middle-aged person who has been in an accident or suffered a debilitating illness might also need long-term care.

Beyond nursing homes, there is a range of services available in the community to help meet long-term care needs. Visiting nurses, home health aides, friendly visitor programs, home-delivered meals, chore services, adult day care centers, and respite services for caregivers who need a break from daily responsibilities can supplement care given by family members.

These services are becoming more widely available. Some or all of them may be found in your community. Your local Area Agency on Aging or Office on Aging can help you locate the services you need. Call the Eldercare Locator at 800-677-1116 to identify your local office.

» Are You Likely to Need Long-Term Care?

You may never need long-term care. But about 19 percent of Americans aged 65 and older experience some degree of chronic physical impairment. Among those aged 85 or older, the proportion of people who are impaired and require long-term care is about 55 percent. In the year 2020, some 12 million older Americans are expected to need long-term care. Most will be cared for at home. Family members and friends are the sole caregivers for 70 percent of elderly people. A study by the U.S. Department of Health and Human Services indicates that people age 65 face at least a 40 percent lifetime risk of entering a nursing home sometime during their lifetime. About 10 percent will stay there five years or longer.

The American population is growing older, and the group over age 85 is now the fastest-growing segment of the population. The odds of entering a nursing home, and staying for longer periods, increase with age. In fact, statistics show that at any given time, 22 percent of those age 85 and older are in a nursing home. Because women generally outlive men by several years, they face a 50 percent greater likelihood than men of entering a nursing home after age 65.

While certainly older people are more likely to need long-term care, your need for long-term care can come at any age. In fact, the U.S. Government Accountability Office estimates that 40 percent of the 13 million people receiving long-term care services are between the ages of 18 and 64.

» What Does Long-Term Care Cost?

Long-term care can be very expensive and the real amount you will spend depends on the level of services you need and the length of time you need care. One year in a nursing home can average more than $50,000. In some regions, it can easily cost twice that amount.

Home care is less expensive but it still adds up. Bringing an aide into your home just three times a week (two to three hours per visit) to help with dressing, bathing, preparing meals, and similar household chores can easily cost $1,000 a month or $12,000 a year. Add in the cost of skilled help, such as physical therapists, and these costs can be much greater.

The average monthly fee assisted living facilities charge is around $2,000. This includes rent and most additional fees. Some residents in the facility may pay significantly more if their care needs are higher.

» Who Pays the Bills?

For the most part, the people who need the care pay the bills. Individuals and their families pay about one-fourth of all nursing home costs out-of-pocket. Generally, long-term care isn't covered by the health insurance you may have either on your own or through your employer.

What about the government? Generally, neither Medicare nor Medicaid cover long-term care. People over 65 and some younger people with disabilities have health coverage through the federal Medicare program. Medicare pays only about 12 percent for short-term skilled nursing home care following hospitalization. Medicare also pays for some skilled at-home care, but only for short-term unstable medical conditions and not for the ongoing assistance that many elderly, ill, or injured people need.

Medicare supplement insurance (often called Medigap or MedSupp) is private insurance that helps cover some of the gaps in Medicare coverage. While these policies help pay the deductible for hospitals and doctors, coinsurance payments, or what Medicare considers excess physician charges, they do not cover long-term care.

Medicaid—the federal program that provides health care coverage to lower-income Americans—pays almost half of all nursing home costs. Medicaid pays benefits either immediately, for people meeting federal poverty guidelines, or after nursing home residents exhaust their savings and become eligible. Turning to Medicaid once meant impoverishing the spouse who remained at home as well as the spouse confined to a nursing home. However, the law permits the at-home spouse to retain specified levels of assets and income.

It's impossible to predict what kind of care you might need in the future, or know exactly what the costs will be. But like other insurance, long-term care insurance allows people to pay a known, affordable premium for a policy to protect against the risk of much larger out-of-pocket expenses.

Since it's likely you will need long-term care, you should learn about the insurance coverage available to help that's most appropriate for you.

» Where Can I Get Long-Term Care Coverage?

Although long-term care insurance is relatively new, more than 100 companies now offer coverage.

Long-term care insurance is generally available through groups and to individuals. Group insurance is typically offered through employers, and this type of coverage is becoming a more common benefit. By the end of 2002, more than 5,600 employers were offering a long-term care insurance plan to their employees, retirees, or both.

Individual long-term care insurance coverage is a good option if you are not employed, work for a small company that doesn't offer a plan, or are self-employed. Choosing a policy requires careful shopping because coverage and costs vary from company to company and depend on the benefit levels you choose.

» What Are the Types of Long-Term Care Policies?

Several types of policies are available. Most are known as "indemnity" or "expense incurred" policies.

An indemnity or "per diem" policy pays up to a fixed benefit amount regardless of what you spend. With an expense-incurred policy, you choose the benefit amount when you buy the policy and you are reimbursed for actual expenses for services received up to a fixed dollar amount per day, week, or month.

Today, many companies also offer "integrated policies" or policies with "pooled benefits." This type of policy provides a total dollar amount that may be used for different types of long-term care services. There is usually a daily, weekly, or monthly dollar limit for your covered long-term care expenses.

For example, say you purchase a policy with a maximum benefit amount of $150,000 of pooled benefits. Under this policy you would have a daily benefit of $150 that would last for 1,000 days if you spend the maximum daily amount on care. If, however, your care costs less, you would receive benefits for more than 1,000 days.

There are no policies that guarantee to cover all expenses fully.

You usually have a choice of daily benefit amounts ranging from $50 to more than $300 per day for nursing home coverage. The daily benefit for at-home care may be less than the benefit for nursing home care. It's important to keep in mind that you are responsible for your actual nursing home or home care costs that exceed the daily benefit amount you purchased.

Because the per-day benefit you buy today may not be enough to cover higher costs years from now, most policies offer inflation adjustments. In many policies, for example, the initial benefit amount will increase automatically each year at a specified rate (such as 5 percent) compounded over the life of the policy.

Some life insurance policies offer long-term care benefits. With these accelerated or living benefits provisions, under certain circumstances a portion of the life insurance benefit is paid to the policyholder for long-term care services instead of to the beneficiary at the policyholder's death. Some companies make these benefits available to all policyholders; others offer them only to people buying new policies.

» What Do Policies Cost?

The cost of long-term care insurance varies widely, depending on the options you choose. For example, inflation adjustments can add between 40 and more than 100 percent to your premium. However, this option can keep benefits in line with the current cost of care.

The actual premium you will pay depends on many factors, including your age, the level of benefits, and the length of time you are willing to wait until benefits begin. A licensed long-term care insurance agent or a financial advisor can help in balancing policy features and premium cost.

Age

In 2002, a policy offering a $150 per day long-term care benefit for four years, with a 90-day deductible, cost a 50-year-old a national average of $564 per year. For someone who was 65 years old, the national average cost was $1,337, and for a 79-year-old, the national average cost was $5,330. The same policy with an inflation protection feature cost, on average nationally, $1,134 at age 50, $2,346 at age 65, and $7,572 at age 79. Please note that these are only national averages. The cost of long-term care varies significantly by state. For the cost of care and coverage in your area, check with a representative of a long-term care insurer, an insurance agent, or financial adviser.

Premiums generally remain the same each year (unless they are increased for an entire class of policyholders at once). That means that the younger you are when you first buy a policy, the lower your annual premium will be.

Benefits

The amount of your premium also depends on the amount of the daily benefit and how long you wish that benefit to be paid. For example, a policy that pays $100 a day for up to five years of long-term care costs more than a policy that pays $50 a day for three years.

Elimination or Deductible Periods

Elimination or deductible periods are the number of days you must be in residence at a nursing home or the number of home care visits you must receive before policy benefits begin. For instance, with a 20-day elimination period your policy will begin paying benefits on the 21st day. Most policies offer a choice of deductible ranging from zero to 180 days. The longer the elimination or deductible period, the lower the premium.

However, longer elimination periods also mean higher out-of-pocket costs. For instance, if have a policy with a 100-day waiting period and you go to a nursing home for a year, you must pay for 100 days of care. If your stay costs $150 a day, your total cost would be $15,000. With a 30-day elimination period, your cost would be only $4,500.

When you're considering a long-term care policy, you should determine, not just how much you can pay for premiums but also how long you could pay for your own care. Bear in mind that while 45 percent of nursing home stays last three months or less, more than one-third last one year or longer. The more costly longer stay may be the devastating financial blow that you may want to insure against.

» Will My Premiums Increase as I Get Older?

In general, premiums will stay the same each year. If they do increase, it will be for the whole class of policyholders, not because you as an individual have aged or your health has deteriorated.

» What Do Long-Term Care Insurance Policies Cover?

Long-term care services are provided when a person cannot perform certain "activities of daily living" (ADLs), or is cognitively impaired because of senile dementia or Alzheimer's disease. Most commonly the ADLs used to determine the need for services include bathing, dressing, transferring (getting from a bed to a chair), toileting, eating, and continence.

Today's policies cover skilled, intermediate, and custodial care in state-licensed nursing homes. Long-term care policies usually also cover home care services such as skilled or nonskilled nursing care, physical therapy, homemakers, and home health aides provided by state-licensed and/or Medicare-certified home health agencies.

Many policies also cover assisted living, adult daycare and other care in the community, alternate care, and respite care for the caregiver.

"Alternate care" is nonconventional care and services developed by a licensed health care practitioner that serve as an alternative to more costly nursing home care. Benefits for alternate care may be available for special medical care and treatments, different sites of care, or medically necessary modifications to the insured's home, like building ramps for wheelchairs or modifications to a kitchen or bathroom. A health care professional develops the alternate plan of care, the insured or insurer may initiate the plan, and the insurer approves it.

You should know that the benefit amount paid for alternate care would reduce the maximum or lifetime benefit available for later confinement in a long-term care facility. Policies may limit the expenses covered under this benefit (for instance, 60 percent of the lifetime maximum limit).

Alzheimer's disease and other organic cognitive disabilities are leading causes for nursing home admissions and worry for many older Americans. These conditions are generally covered under long-term care policies.

» What Is Not Covered?

All policies contain limits and exclusions to keep premiums reasonable and affordable. These are likely to differ from policy to policy. Before you buy, be sure you understand exactly what is and is not covered under a particular policy.

Preexisting Conditions

Preexisting conditions are health problems you had when you became insured. Insurance companies may require that a period of time pass before the policy pays for care related to these conditions. For example, a company may exclude coverage of preexisting conditions for six months. This means that if you need long-term care within six months of the policy's issue date for that condition, you may be denied benefits. Companies do not generally exclude coverage for preexisting conditions for more than six months.

Specific Exclusions

Some mental and nervous disorders are not covered. Alcoholism and drug abuse are usually not covered, along with care needed after an intentionally selfinflicted injury. Virtually all policies now cover Alzheimer's disease and no longer require a hospital stay before paying nursing home benefits.

» What Else Should I Know Before I Buy?

Different options are available under different policies. These are:

Eligibility

If you are in reasonably good health and can take care of yourself and if you are between the ages of 18 and 84, you can probably buy long-term care insurance. Some companies do not sell individual policies to people under age 18 or over age 84. Age limitations apply only to your age at the time of purchase, not at the time you use the benefits.

Duration or Dollar Limitations of Benefits

Long-term care policies generally limit benefits to a maximum dollar amount or a maximum number of days and may have separate benefit limits for nursing home, assisted living facility, and home health care within the same policy. For example, a policy may offer $100 per day up to five years of nursing home coverage (many policies now offer lifetime nursing home coverage) and only up to $80 per day up to five years of assisted living and home health care coverage.

Generally, there are two ways a company defines a policy's maximum benefit period. Under one definition, a policy may offer a one-time maximum benefit period. A policy with five years of nursing home coverage, issued by a company using this definition, would pay only for a total of five years in a policyholder's lifetime.

Other policies offer a maximum benefit period for each "period of disability." A policy with a five-year maximum benefit period would cover more than one nursing home stay lasting up to five years each if the periods of disability were separated by six months or more.

Renewability

Virtually all long-term care policies sold to individuals are guaranteed renewable; they cannot be canceled as long as you pay your premiums on time and as long as you have told the truth about your health on the application. Premiums can be increased, however, if they are increased for an entire group of policyholders.

The renewability provision, normally found on the first page of the policy, specifies under what conditions the policy can be canceled and when premiums may increase.

Nonforfeiture Benefits

This benefit returns to policyholders some of their benefits if they drop their coverage. Most companies now offer this option. The most common types of nonforfeiture benefits offered today are "return of premium" or a "shortened benefit period."

With a "return of premium" benefit, the policyholder receives cash, usually a percent of the total premiums paid to date after lapse or death. With a "shortened benefit period," the long-term care coverage continues but the benefit period or duration amount is reduced as specified in the policy. A nonforfeiture benefit can add from 20 to 100 percent to a policy's cost.

Some policies may offer "contingent nonforfeiture benefits upon lapse," a feature that gives policyholders additional options in the face of a significant increase in policy premiums. If you do not purchase the optional nonforfeiture benefit, then a contingent nonforfeiture benefit is triggered if policy premiums rise by a specified percentage. For example, if, at age 70, your premium rises to 40 percent above the original premium, you have the option of either decreasing the amount your policy pays per day of care or of converting to a policy with a shorter duration of benefits.

Waiver of Premium

This provision allows you to stop paying premiums during the time you are receiving benefits. Read the policy carefully to see if there are any restrictions on this provision, such as a requirement to be in a nursing home for any length of time (90 days is a typical requirement) or receiving home health care before premiums are waived.

Disclosure

Your medical history is very important because the insurance company uses the information you provide on your application to assess your eligibility for coverage. The application must be accurate and complete. If it is not, the insurance company may be within its rights to deny coverage when you file a claim. In fact, many companies now waive the preexisting condition requirement if you fully disclose your medical history and are issued a policy.

» What About Switching Policies?

New long-term care insurance policies may have more favorable provisions than older policies. Newer policies, for instance, generally do not require prior hospital stays or certain levels of care before benefits begin. But, if you do switch, preexisting condition exclusions for specified periods of time will have to begin again. In addition, your new premiums may be higher because they will be based on your current age.

You should never switch policies before making sure the new policy is better than the one you already have. And you should never drop an old policy before making sure the new one is in force.

» What Should I Look for in a Policy?

The National Association of Insurance Commissioners has developed standards that protect consumers. You should look for a policy that includes:

■ At least one year of nursing home or home health care coverage, including intermediate and custodial care. Nursing home or home health care benefits should not be limited primarily to skilled care.
■ Coverage for Alzheimer's disease, if the policyholder develops it after purchasing the policy.
■ An inflation protection option. The policy should offer a choice among:
  —automatically increasing the initial benefit level on an annual basis, or
  —a guaranteed right to increase benefit levels periodically without providing evidence of insurability.

■ An "outline of coverage" that describes in detail the policy's benefits, limitations, and exclusions, and also allows you to compare it with others. A long-term care insurance shopper's guide that helps you decide whether long-term care insurance is appropriate for you. Your company or agent should provide both of these.

■ A guarantee that the policy cannot be canceled, nonrenewed, or otherwise terminated because you get older or suffer deterioration in physical or mental health.

- The right to return the policy for any reason within 30 days after you have purchased the policy and to receive a premium refund.

- No requirement that policyholders:
  —first be hospitalized in order to receive nursing home benefits or home health care benefits,
  —first receive skilled nursing home care before receiving intermediate or custodial nursing home care, or
  —first receive nursing home care before receiving benefits for home health care.

» Before You Buy

Insurance policies are legal contracts. Read and compare the policies you are considering before you buy, and make sure you understand all of the provisions. Marketing or sales literature is no substitute for the actual policy. Read the policy itself before you buy.

Discuss the policies you are considering with people whose opinions you respect—perhaps your doctor, financial advisor, your children, or an informed friend or relative.

Ask for the insurance company's financial rating and for a summary of each policy's benefits or an outline of coverage. (Ratings result from analyses of a company's financial records.) Good agents and good insurance companies want you to know what you are buying.

And bear in mind: Even after you buy a policy, if you find that it does not meet your needs you generally have 30 days to return the policy and get your money back. This is called the "free look" period.

Don't give in to high-pressure sales tactics. Don't be afraid to ask your insurance agent to explain anything that is unclear. If you are not satisfied with an agent's answers, ask for someone to contact in the company itself. Call your state insurance department if you are not satisfied with the answers you get from the agent or from company representatives.

» Long-Term Care Policy Checklist

Before you begin shopping, you should find out how much nursing home or home health care costs in your area today. If you needed care right away could you find it locally or would you have to go to another, potentially more expensive area? Once you've done some research, you can use the following checklist to help you compare policies you may be considering.

1. What services are covered?
   - Nursing home care
   - Home health care
   - Assisted living facility
   - Adult daycare
   - Alternate care
   - Respite care
   - Other

2. How much does the policy pay per day for nursing home care? For home health care? For an assisted living facility? For adult daycare? For alternate care? For respite care? Other?

3. How long will benefits last in a nursing home? At home? In an assisted living facility? Other?

4. Does the policy have a maximum lifetime benefit? If so, what is it for nursing home care? For home health care? For an assisted living facility? Other?

5. Does the policy have a maximum length of coverage for each period of confinement? If so, what is it for nursing home care? For home health care? For an assisted living facility?

6. How long must I wait before preexisting conditions are covered?

7. How many days must I wait before benefits begin for nursing home care? For home health care? For an assisted living facility? Other?

8. Are Alzheimer's disease and other organic mental and nervous disorders covered?

9. Does this policy require: An assessment of activities of daily living? An assessment of cognitive impairment? Physician certification of need? A prior hospital stay for nursing home care? Home health care? A prior nursing home stay for home health care coverage? Other?

10. Is the policy guaranteed renewable?

11. What is the age range for enrollment?

12. Is there a waiver-of-premium provision for nursing home care? For home health care?

13. How long must I be confined before premiums are waived?

14. Does the policy have a nonforfeiture benefit?

15. Does the policy offer an inflation adjustment feature? If so, what is the rate of increase? How often is it applied? For how long? Is there an additional cost?

16. What does the policy cost?
    - Per year?
      —With inflation feature
      —Without inflation feature
      —With nonforfeiture feature
      —Without nonforfeiture feature
    - Per month?
      —With inflation feature
      —Without inflation feature
      —With nonforfeiture feature
      —Without nonforfeiture feature

17. Is there a 30-day free look?

» HIPAA's Impact on Long-Term Care Insurance

The Health Insurance Portability and Accountability Act of 1996 (HIPAA) affects how premiums and benefits are taxed and offers consumer protection standards for long-term care insurance. The following are answers to commonly asked questions about HIPAA.

Tax Treatment

Q: What is tax clarification for private long-term care insurance and why is it necessary?

A: The clarifications assure that, like major medical coverage, benefits from qualified long-term care insurance plans generally are not taxed. Without HIPAA clarifications, these benefits might be considered taxable income.

Q: Will consumers be able to take a tax deduction for the premiums they pay on a tax-qualified longterm care insurance policy? Can consumers deduct from their taxes costs associated with receiving long-term care?

A: The answer to both questions is "yes." HIPAA says that qualified long-term care insurance will now receive the same tax treatment as accident and health insurance. That means that premiums for long-term care insurance, as well as consumers' out-of-pocket expenses for long-term care, can be applied toward meeting the federal tax codes' 7.5 percent floor for medical expense deductions. However, there are limits, based on a policyholder's age, for the total amount of long-term care premiums that can be applied toward the 7.5 percent minimum. (Check with your financial planner or tax adviser to see if you are eligible to take this deduction.)

Q: Will employers be able to deduct anything for the cost of providing or paying for qualified long-term care insurance for their employees?

A: Generally, employers will be able to deduct, as a business expense, both the cost of setting up a long-term care insurance plan for their employees and the contributions that they may make toward paying for the cost of premiums.

Q: Will employer contributions be excluded from the taxable income of employees?

A: Yes.

Q: Can Individual Retirement Accounts (IRAs) and 401k funds be used to purchase private long-term care insurance?

A: No. However, under a demonstration project, tax-free funds deposited in Medical Savings Accounts can be used to pay long-term care insurance premiums.

Consumer Protection Standards

Q: What is the connection between consumer protection standards and tax treatment of long-term care plans?

A: To qualify for favorable tax treatment, a long-term care policy sold after 1996 must contain the consumer protection standards spelled out in HIPAA. Also, insurance companies must follow certain administrative and marketing practices or face significant fines. Generally speaking, policies sold prior to January 1, 1997, automatically will be eligible for favorable tax treatment. Lastly, nothing in the new law prevents states from imposing more stringent consumer protection standards.

Q: What kinds of consumer protections must insurance companies employ to meet HIPAA standards?

A: There are several. Consumers must receive a "Shopper's Guide" and a description of the policy's benefits and limitations (i.e., Outline of Coverage) early in the sales process. The Outline of Coverage allows consumers to compare policies from different companies. Companies must report annually the number of claims denied and information on policy replacements and terminations. Sales practices such as "twisting"—knowingly making misleading or incomplete comparisons of policies—are prohibited, as are high-pressure sales tactics.

Q: Do the HIPAA standards address limits on benefits and exclusions from coverage?

A: Yes. According to HIPAA, no policy can be sold as a long-term care insurance policy if it limits or excludes coverage by type of treatment, medical condition, or accident. However, there are several exceptions to this rule. For example, policies may limit or exclude coverage for preexisting conditions or diseases, mental or nervous disorders (but not Alzheimer's), or alcoholism or drug addiction. A policy cannot, however, exclude coverage for preexisting conditions for more than six months after the effective date of coverage.

Q: What will prevent a company from canceling my policy when I need it?

A: The law prohibits a company from not renewing a policy except for nonpayment of premiums. Policies cannot be canceled because of age or deterioration of mental or physical health. In fact, if a policyholder is late paying a premium, the policy can be reinstated up to five months later if the reason for nonpayment is shown to be cognitive impairment.

Q: Will these standards help people who, for whatever reason, lose their group coverage?

A: They will. People covered by a group policy will be allowed to continue their coverage when they leave their employer, so long as they pay their premiums in a timely fashion. Further, an individual who has been covered under a group plan for at least six months may convert to an individual policy if and when the group plan is discontinued. The individual may do so without providing evidence of insurability.

» If You Need Help

Every state has a department of insurance that regulates insurers and assists consumers. If you need more information or if you want to register a complaint, check the government listings in your local phone book for your state's department of insurance.

Additional information about long-term care is available from the Area Agency on Aging. For your local office, call 1-800-677-1116. Other sources include:

American Health Care Association
1201 L Street, NW
Washington, DC 20005
(202) 842-4444
www.ahca.org

National Association of Insurance Commissioners
2301 McGee Street, Suite 800
Kansas City, MO 64108
(816) 842-3600
www.naic.org

National Council on the Aging
300 D Street, SW, Suite 801
Washington, DC 20024
(202) 479-1200
www.ncoa.org

University of Minnesota Extension Service
www.financinglongtermcare. umn.edu

For more information

■ You can find AHIP online at *www.ahip.org*. This site offers additional consumer information about long-term care insurance and other insurance coverage.

■ To find a long-term care insurance agent or financial adviser near you who has earned the Long-Term Care Professional (LTCP) designation, call AHIP's Insurance Education Program at 202-778-8471.

Reviewed by Cooperative State Research, Education, and Extension Service, U.S. Department of Agriculture, in cooperation with long-term care insurance experts Mary Ellen Rider, Ph.D., Extension Specialist, Consumer Health Policy, University of Nebraska-Lincoln; Marlene Stum, Ph.D., Family Resource Management Specialist, University of Minnesota; and Paul McNamara, Ph.D., University of Illinois.

Although frequently revised, this booklet contains information that is subject to changing federal and state law. AHIP provides this booklet for guidance only; it is not a substitute for the advice of licensed insurance professionals and legal counsel.

A Shopper's Guide to Long-Term Care Insurance

National Association of Insurance Commissioners (NAIC)
Revised 2003

» About the NAIC

The National Association of Insurance Commissioners (NAIC) is the oldest association of state government officials. Its members consist of the chief insurance regulators in all 50 states, the District of Columbia and four U.S. territories. The primary responsibility of the state regulators is to protect the interests of insurance consumers, and the NAIC helps regulators fulfill that obligation in a number of different ways. This guide is one example of work done by the NAIC to assist states in educating and protecting consumers.

Another way the NAIC lends support to state regulators is by providing a forum for the development of uniform public policy when uniformity is appropriate. It does this through a series of model laws, regulations and guidelines, developed for the states' use. States that choose to do so may adopt the models intact or modify them to meet the needs of their marketplace and consumers. As you read through this guide, you will find several references to such NAIC model laws or regulations related to long-term care insurance. You may check with your state insurance department to find out if these NAIC models have been enacted in your state.

National Association of Insurance Commissioners
2301 McGee Street, Suite 800, Kansas City, MO 64108-2604
(816) 842-3600   Fax: (816) 783-8175   *www.naic.org*

» Table of Contents

» About This Shopper's Guide

The **National Association of Insurance Commissioners** (NAIC) has written this guide to help you understand long-term care and the insurance options that can help you pay for long-term care services. The decision to buy long-term care insurance is very important and one you shouldn't make in a hurry. In most states, state law requires insurance companies or agents to give you this guide to help you better understand long-term care insurance and decide which, if any, policy to buy. Some states produce their own guide.

Take a moment to look at the table of contents and you'll see the questions this guide answers and the information that is in it. Then, read the guide carefully. If you see a term you don't understand, look in the glossary starting on page 275. (Terms in **bold** in the text are in the glossary.) Take your time. Decide if buying a policy might be right for you. If you decide to shop for a long-term care insurance policy, start by getting information about the long-term care services and facilities you might use and how much they charge. Use the first worksheet that starts on page 284 to write down this information. Then, as you shop for a policy, use Worksheet 2, starting on page 286. There you can write down the information you collect to compare policies and buy the one that best meets your needs.

If you have questions, call your state insurance department or the insurance counseling program in your state. The telephone numbers are listed starting on page 301 of this guide.

» What Is Long-Term Care?

Someone with a prolonged physical illness, a disability, or a **cognitive impairment** (such as **Alzheimer's disease**) often needs long-term care. Many different services help people with chronic conditions overcome limitations that keep them from being independent. Long-term care is different from traditional medical care. Long-term care helps one live as he or she is now; it may not help to improve or correct medical problems. Long-term care services may include help with **activities of daily living, home health care, respite care, hospice care, adult day care,** care in a

nursing home, and care in an **assisted living facility.** Long-term care may also include care management services, which will evaluate your needs and coordinate and monitor the delivery of long-term care services. Someone with a physical illness or disability often needs **hands-on** or **stand-by assistance** with activities of daily living (see page 254). People with cognitive impairments usually need supervision, protection, or verbal reminders to do everyday activities. The way long-term care services are provided is changing. Skilled care and personal care are still the terms used most often to describe long-term care and the type or level of care you may need.

People usually need **skilled care** for medical conditions that require care by medical personnel such as registered nurses or professional therapists. This care is usually needed 24 hours a day, a physician must order it, and the care must follow a plan. Individuals usually get skilled care in a nursing home but may also receive it in other places. For example, you might get skilled care in your home with help from visiting nurses or therapists. Examples of skilled care including physical therapy, caring for a wound, or supervising the administration of intravenous medication.

NOTE: **Medicare** and **Medicaid** have their own definitions of skilled care. Please refer to *The Guide to Health Insurance for People with Medicare* or *The Medicare Handbook* to find out how Medicare defines skilled care. Contact your local social services office for questions about Medicaid's definition of skilled care. For copies of these publications, contact your state insurance department or **State Health Insurance Assistance Program** listed on page 301.

Personal care (sometimes called custodial care) helps one with activities of daily living (ADLs.) These activities include bathing, eating, dressing, toileting, continence, and transferring. Personal care is less involved than skilled care, and it may be given in many settings.

» How Much Does Long-Term Care Cost?

Long-term care can be expensive. The cost depends on the amount and type of care you need and where you get it. Below are some average annual costs for care provided in a nursing home, in an assisted living facility and in your own home.

Nursing Home Costs

In 2001, the national average cost of nursing home care was $56,000 per year,[1] or about $153 per day. This cost does not include items such as therapies and medications, which could make the cost much higher.

Assisted Living Facility Costs

In 2001, assisted living facilities reported charging an average fee of $1,873 per month, or $22,476 per year, including rent and most other fees.[2] Some residents in the facilities may pay a lot more if their care needs are higher.

Home Care Costs

In 2001, the national average cost of part-time basic home care ranged from $12,000 to $16,000 per year.[3] Skilled care provided by a nurse is more expensive than care provided by a home health aide. Annual costs for home health care will vary based on the number of days per week the caregiver visits, the type of care required and the length of each visit. Home health care can be expensive if round-the-clock care is required. These costs are different across the country. Your state insurance department or the insurance counseling program in your state may have costs for your area. (See directory starting on page 301.)

» Who Pays for Long-Term Care?

People pay for long-term care in a variety of ways. These include: using the personal resources of individuals or their families, long-term care insurance, and some assistance from **Medicaid** for those who qualify. **Medicare, Medicare supplement insurance**, and the health insurance you may have at work usually *will not pay* for long-term care.

Individual Personal Resources

Individuals and their families generally pay for part or all of the costs of long-term care from their own funds. Many use savings and investments. Some people sell assets, such as their homes, to pay for their long-term care needs.

Medicare

Medicare's skilled nursing facility (SNF) benefit does not cover most nursing home care.[4] Medicare will pay the cost of some skilled care in an approved nursing home or in your home but only in specific situations. The SNF benefit only covers you if a medical professional says you need daily skilled care after you have been in the hospital for at least three days and you are receiving that care in a nursing home that is a Medicare-certified skilled nursing facility. While Medicare may cover *up to 100 days* of skilled nursing home care per benefit period when these conditions are met, after 20 days beneficiaries must pay a coinsurance fee. In 2002, that coinsurance was $101.50 per day.[5] While Medicare may pay for nursing home care sometimes, it doesn't cover the costs of care in assisted living facilities.

While many people would like to receive care in their own homes, Medicare does not cover **homemaker services**. In addition, Medicare doesn't pay for home health aides to give you **personal care** unless you are homebound and are also getting skilled care such as nursing or therapy. The personal care must also relate to the treatment of an illness or injury and you can only get a limited amount of care in any week.

You should not rely on Medicare to pay for your long-term care needs.

Medicare Supplement Insurance

Medicare supplement insurance is private insurance that helps pay for some of the gaps in Medicare coverage, such as hospital deductibles and excess physicians' charges above what Medicare approves. Medicare supplement policies do not cover long-term care costs. However, four Medicare supplement policies—Plans D, G, I, and J—do pay up to $1,600 per year[6] for services to people recovering at home from an illness, injury, or surgery. The benefit will pay for short-term, at-home help with activities of daily living. You must qualify for Medicare-covered home health services before this Medicare supplement benefit is available.

Medicaid

Medicaid is the government-funded program that pays nursing home care only for individuals who are low income and who have spent most of their assets. Medicaid pays for nearly half of all nursing home care on an aggregate basis, but many people who need long-term care never qualify for Medicaid assistance.[7] Medicaid also pays for some home and **community-based services**. To get Medicaid help, you must meet federal and state guidelines for income and assets. Many people start paying for nursing home care out of their own funds and "**spend down**" their income until they are eligible for Medicaid. Medicaid may then pay part or all of their nursing home costs. You may have to use up most of your assets on your health care before Medicaid is able to help. Some assets and income can be protected for a spouse who remains at home. In addition, some of your assets may be protected if you have long-term care insurance approved under one of the state programs. (See section on "Other Options" on page 244.)

State laws differ about how much money and assets you can keep and be eligible for Medicaid. (Some assets, such as your home, may not count when deciding if you are eligible for Medicaid.) However, federal law requires your state to recover from your estate the costs of the Medicaid-paid benefits you receive.[8] *Contact your state Medicaid office, office on aging, or state department of social services to learn about the rules in your state. The insurance counseling program in your state also may have some Medicaid information.* (Please see the list of offices on aging and counseling programs on page 301.)

Long-Term Care Insurance

Long-term care insurance is one other way you may pay for long-term care. This type of insurance will pay for some or all of your long-term care. It was introduced in the 1980s as nursing home insurance but has changed a lot and now covers much more than nursing home care. The rest of this Shopper's Guide will give you information on long-term care insurance. You should know that a federal law, the **Health Insurance Portability and Accountability Act** of 1996, or HIPAA, gives some federal income tax advantages to people who buy certain long-term care insurance policies. These policies are called Tax-Qualified Long-Term Care Insurance Contracts, or simply Qualified Contracts. The tax advantages of these policies are outlined on page 245. There may be other tax advantages in your state. *You should check with your state insurance department or insur-*

ance counseling program for information about tax-qualified policies. (Please see the list of state insurance departments and counseling programs on page 301.) Check with your tax advisor to find out if the tax advantages make sense for you.

» Who May Need Long-Term Care?

The need for long-term care may begin gradually as you find that you need more and more help with activities of daily living, such as bathing and dressing. Or you may suddenly need long-term care after a major illness, such as a stroke or a heart attack.

If you do need care, you may need nursing home or home health care for only a short time. Or, you may need these services for many months, years, or the rest of your life.

It is hard to know if and when you will need long-term care, but there are some statistics that may help. *For example:*

■ Life expectancy after age 65 has now increased to 17.9 years, up from 1940 when life expectancy after 65 was only 13 extra years. The longer people live, the greater the chances they will need assistance due to chronic conditions.[9]

■ About 12.8 million Americans of all ages require long-term care, but only 2.4 million live in nursing homes.[10]

■ About 44% of people reaching age 65 are expected to enter a nursing home at least once in their lifetime.[11] Of those who do enter a nursing home about 53% will stay for one year or more.[12]

» Do You Need Long-Term Care Insurance?

Whether you should buy a long-term care insurance policy will depend on your age, health status, overall retirement goals, income, and assets. For instance, if your only source of income is a Social Security benefit or Supplemental Security Income (SSI), you probably shouldn't buy long-term care insurance since you may not be able to afford the premium.

Is Long-Term Care Insurance Right For You?

You should *not* buy long-term care insurance if:
- You can't afford the premiums.
- You have limited assets.
- Your only source of income is a Social Security benefit or Supplemental Security Income (SSI).
- You often have trouble paying for utilities, food, medicine, or other important needs.
- You are on Medicaid.

You should *consider* buying long-term care insurance if:
- You have significant assets and income.
- You want to protect some of your assets and income.
- You can pay premiums, including possible premium increases, without financial difficulty.
- You want to stay independent of the support of others.
- You want to have the flexibility of choosing care in the setting you prefer or will be most comfortable in.

On the other hand, if you have a large amount of assets but don't want to use them to pay for long-term care, you may want to buy a long-term care insurance policy. Many people buy a policy because they want to stay independent of government aid or the help of family. They don't want to burden anyone with having to care for them. However, you should not buy a policy if you can't afford the premium or aren't sure you can pay the premium for the rest of your life.

If you already have health problems that are likely to mean you will need long-term care (for example, Alzheimer's disease or Parkinson's disease), you probably won't be able to buy a policy. Insurance companies have medical **underwriting** standards to keep the cost of long-term care insurance affordable. Without such standards, most people would not buy coverage until they needed long-term care services.

Some states have a regulation requiring the insurance company and the agent to go through a worksheet with you to decide if long-term care insurance is right for you. The worksheet describes the premium for the policy you're thinking about buying and asks you questions about the source and amount of your income and the amount of your savings and investments. Some states require that you fill out the worksheet and send it to the insurance company. Even if you aren't required to fill out this worksheet, it might help you decide if long-term care insurance is right for you.

Remember, not everyone should buy a long-term care insurance policy. For some, a policy is affordable and worth the cost. For others, the cost is too great, or the policy they can afford doesn't offer enough benefits to make it worthwhile. You should not buy long-term care insurance if the only way you can afford to pay for it is by not paying other important bills. Look closely at your needs and resources, and discuss it with a family member to decide if long-term care insurance is right for you. (There are several worksheets at the back of this book that will help you as you think about whether you should buy long-term care insurance).

For further determination of whether you should or should not consider buying long-term care insurance, please refer to the Personal Worksheet found in the back of this Shopper's Guide. In addition to the personal worksheet, consumer worksheets #1 through #4 should be used to help you decide.

If, after careful consideration, you decide that long-term care insurance is right for you, check out the company and the agent, if one is involved, before you buy a policy. Insurance companies and agents must be licensed in your state to sell long-term care insurance. If you're not sure, contact your state insurance department. (Please see the list of state insurance departments starting on page 301.)

» How Can You Buy Long-Term Care Insurance?

Private insurance companies sell long-term care insurance policies. You can buy an individual policy from an agent or through the mail. Or, you can buy coverage under a group policy through an employer or through membership in an association. The federal government and several state governments offer long-term care insurance coverage to their employees, retirees and their families. This program is voluntary and premiums are paid by participants. You can also get long-term care benefits through a life insurance policy.

Individual Policies

Today, most long-term care insurance policies are sold to individuals. Insurance agents sell many of these policies but companies also sell policies through the mail or by telephone. You will find that individual policies can be very different from one company to the next. Each company may also offer policies with different combinations of benefits. Be sure to shop among policies, companies and agents to get the coverage that best fits your needs.

Policies from Your Employer

Your employer may offer a group long-term care insurance plan or offer individual policies at a group discount. An increasing number of employers offer this benefit,[13] especially since the passage of the Health Insurance Portability and Accountability Act (HIPAA). HIPAA allows employers the same type of federal tax benefit when they pay for their employee's long-term care insurance as when they pay for their health insurance (except for Section 125 cafeteria plans).

The employer-group plan may be similar to what you could buy in an individual policy. If you are an active employee, one advantage of an employer-group plan is you may not have to meet any medical requirements to get a policy or there may be a relaxed screening process for active employees. Many employers also let retirees, spouses, parents, and parents-in-law apply for this coverage. Relatives must usually pass the company's medical screening to qualify for coverage and must pay the premium.

Generally, insurance companies must let you keep your coverage after your employment ends or your employer cancels the group plan. In most cases, you will be able to continue your coverage or convert it to another long-term care insurance policy. Your premiums and benefits may change, however.

If an employer offers long-term care insurance, be sure to think about it carefully. An employer-group policy may offer you options you can't find if you buy a policy on your own.

Federal Government

Federal and U.S. Postal Service employees and annuitants, members and retired members of the uniformed services, and qualified relatives are eligible to apply for long-term care insurance coverage under the Federal Long-Term Care Insurance Program. Private insurance companies underwrite the insurance, and the federal government does not pay any of the premiums. The group rates under this program may or may not be lower than individual rates and the benefits may also be different.[14]

State Government

If you or a member of your family is a state or public employee or retiree, you may be able to buy long-term care insurance under a state government program.

Association Policies

Many associations let insurance companies and agents offer long-term care insurance to their members. These policies are like other types of long-term care insurance and typically require medical underwriting. Like employer-group policies, association policies usually give their members a choice of benefit options. In most cases, policies sold through associations must let members keep or convert their coverage after leaving the association. Be careful about joining an association just to buy any insurance coverage. Review your rights if the policy is terminated or canceled.

Policies Sponsored by Continuing Care Retirement Communities

Many **Continuing Care Retirement Communities** (CCRC) offer or require you to buy long-term care insurance. A CCRC is a retirement complex that offers a broad range of services and levels of care. You must be a resident or on the waiting list of a CCRC and meet the insurance company's medical requirements to buy its long-term care insurance policy. The coverage will be similar to other group or individual policies.

Life Insurance Policies

Some companies let you use your life insurance death benefit to pay for specific conditions such as terminal illness or for qualified long-term care expenses such as home health care, assisted living, or nursing home care. A life insurance death benefit you use while you are alive is known as an accelerated death benefit. A life insurance policy that uses an **accelerated death benefit** to pay for long-term care expenses may also be known as a "life/long-term care" policy. It may be an individual or a group life insurance policy. The company pays you the actual charges for care when you receive long-term care services, but no more than a certain percent of the policy's death benefit per day or per month. Policies may pay part or all of the death benefit for qualified long-term care expenses. Some companies let you buy more long-term care coverage than the amount of your death benefit in the form of a **rider**.

Some policies may allow you to withdraw the cash value of your policy to pay for specific conditions and expenses. It is important to remember that if you use money from your life insurance policy to pay for long-term care, it will reduce the death benefit the beneficiary will get. For example, if you buy a policy with a $100,000 death benefit, using $60,000 for long-term care will cut the death benefit of your policy to $40,000. It may also affect the cash value of your policy. Ask your agent how this may affect other aspects of your life insurance policy. If you bought life insurance to meet a specific need after your death, your survivors may not be able to meet that need if you use your policy to pay for long-term care. If you never use the long-term care benefit, the policy will pay the full death benefit to your beneficiary.

Other Options

Some states have long-term care insurance programs designed to help people with the financial impact of spending down to meet Medicaid eligibility standards. Under these programs (sometimes called "**partnership programs**"), when you buy a specially approved insurance policy, you will receive full or partial protection against the normal Medicaid requirement to spend down your assets to become eligible. *Check with your state insurance department or counseling program to see if these policies are available in your state.* Please keep in mind that these programs have specific requirements in each state in which they are offered.

» What Types of Policies Can I Buy?

You may be asked to choose between a "tax-qualified" long-term care insurance policy and one that is "non-tax-qualified." There are important differences between the two types of policies. These differences were created by the Health Insurance Portability and Accountability Act (HIPAA). A federally tax-qualified long-term care insurance policy, or a qualified policy, offers certain federal income tax advantages. If you have a qualified long-term care policy, and you itemize your deductions, you may be able to deduct part or all of the premium you pay for the policy. You may be able to add the premium to your other deductible medical expenses. You may then be able to deduct the amount that is more than 7.5% of your adjusted gross income on your federal income tax return. The amount depends on your age, as shown in the table.

Regardless of which policy you choose, make sure that you understand how the **benefits** and **triggers** will work and that they are acceptable to you. For example, benefits paid by a qualified long-term care insurance policy are generally not taxable as income. Benefits from a long-term care insurance policy that is not qualified may be taxable as income.

If you bought a long-term care insurance policy before January 1, 1997, that policy is probably qualified. HIPAA allowed these policies to be "grandfathered," or considered qualified, even though they may not meet all of the standards that new policies must meet to be qualified. The tax

Your Age	Maximum Amount That You Can Claim
40 years old or younger	$250
More than 40 but not more than 50	$470
More than 50 but not more than 60	$940
More than 60 but not more than 70	$2,510
More than 70	$3,130

2003 figures.[15] These amounts will increase annually based on the Medical Consumer Price Index.

advantages are the same whether the policy was sold before or after 1997. You should carefully examine the advantages and disadvantages of trading a grandfathered policy for a new policy. In most cases, it will be to your advantage to keep your old policy.

Long-term care insurance policies that are sold on or after January 1, 1997, as tax-qualified must meet certain federal standards. To be qualified, policies must be labeled as tax-qualified, must be **guaranteed renewable**, include a number of consumer protection provisions, cover only qualified long-term care services, and generally *can provide only limited cash surrender values*. (See **Benefit Triggers**, page 253.)

Qualified long-term care services are those generally given by long-term care providers. These services must be required by chronically ill individuals and must be given according to a plan of care prescribed by a licensed health care practitioner.

You are considered **chronically ill** if you are expected to be unable to do at least two activities of daily living without substantial assistance from another person for at least 90 days. Another way you may be considered to be chronically ill is if you need **substantial supervision** to protect your health and safety because you have a cognitive impairment. A policy issued to you before January 1, 1997, doesn't have to define chronically ill this way. (See Benefit Triggers, page 253.)

Some life insurance policies with long-term care benefits may be tax-qualified. You may be able to deduct the premium you pay for the long-term care benefits that a life insurance policy provides. However, be sure to check with your personal tax advisor to learn how much of the premium can be deducted as a medical expense.

The long-term care benefits paid from a tax-qualified life insurance policy with long-term care benefits are generally not taxable as income. Tax-qualified life insurance policies with long-term care benefits must meet the same federal standards as other tax-qualified policies, including the requirement that you must be chronically ill to receive benefits.

Federally Tax-Qualified Policies	Federally Non-Tax-Qualified Policies
1. Premiums can be included with other annual uncompensated medical expenses for deductions from your income in excess of 7.5% of adjusted gross income up to a maximum amount adjusted for inflation.	1. You may or may not be able to deduct any part of your annual premiums. Congress and the U.S. Department of the Treasury have not clarified this area of the law.
2. Benefits that you receive and use to pay for long-term care services generally will not be counted as income. For policies that pay benefits using the expense-incurred method, benefits that you receive in excess of the costs of long-term care services may be taxable. For policies that pay benefits using the indemnity or disability methods, all benefit payments up to the federally approved per diem (daily) rate are tax-free even if they exceed your expenses.	2. Benefits that you receive may or may not count as income. Congress and the U.S. Department of the Treasury have not clarified this area of the law.
3. To trigger the benefits under your policy, the federal law requires you to be unable to do two ADLs without substantial assistance.	3. Policies can offer a different combination of benefit triggers. Benefit triggers are not restricted to two ADLs.
4. "Medical necessity" can't be used as a trigger for benefits.	4. "Medical necessity" and/or other measures of disability can be offered as benefit triggers.
5. Chronic illness or disability must be expected to last for at least 90 days.	5. Policies don't have to require that the disability be expected to last for at least 90 days.
6. For cognitive impairment to be covered, a person must require "substantial supervision."	6. Policies don't have to require "substantial supervision" to trigger benefits for cognitive impairments.

Whether you are considering buying a tax-qualified or a non-tax-qualified policy, consult with your tax consultant or legal advisor regarding the tax consequences in your situation.

» How Do Long-Term Care Insurance Policies Work?

Long-term care insurance policies are not standardized like Medicare supplement insurance. Companies sell policies that combine benefits and coverage in different ways.

How Benefits Are Paid

Insurance companies that sell long-term care insurance generally pay benefits using one of three different methods: **the expense-incurred method**, the **indemnity method**, or the **disability method**. It is important to read the literature that accompanies your policy (or certificate for group policies) and to compare the benefits and premiums.

When the **expense-incurred method** is used, the insurance company must decide if you are eligible for benefits and if your claim is for eligible services. Your policy or certificate will pay benefits only when you receive eligible services. Once you have incurred an expense for an eligible service, benefits are paid either to you or your provider. The coverage will pay for the lesser of the expense you incurred or the dollar limit of your policy. Most policies bought today pay benefits using the expense incurred method.

When the **indemnity method** is used, the benefit is a set dollar amount. The benefit is not based on the specific services received or on the expenses incurred. The insurance company only needs to decide if you are eligible for benefits and if the services you are receiving are covered by the policy. Once the company decides you are eligible *and* you are receiving eligible long-term care services, the insurance company will pay that set amount directly to you up to the limit of the policy. When the **disability method** is used, you are only required to meet the benefit eligibility criteria. Once you do, you receive your full daily benefit, even if you are not receiving any long-term care services.

Pooled Benefits and Joint Policies

You may be able to buy a long-term care insurance policy that covers more than just one person, or more than one kind of long-term care service. The benefits provided by these policies are often called "pooled benefits." One type of pooled benefit covers more than one person, such as a husband and wife, or two partners, or two or more related adults. This type of benefit is sometimes called a "joint policy" or a "joint benefit." This pooled benefit usually has a total benefit that applies to all of the individuals covered by the policy. If one of the covered individuals collects benefits, that amount is subtracted from the total policy benefit. For example, if a husband and wife have a policy that provides $150,000 in total long-term care benefits, and the husband uses $25,000 in benefits from the policy, $125,000 would be left to pay benefits for either the husband or the wife, or both.

Another kind of "pooled benefit" provides a total dollar amount that can be used for various long-term care services. These policies pay a daily, weekly, or monthly dollar limit for one or more covered services. You can combine benefits in ways that best meet your needs. This gives you more control over how your benefits are spent. For example, you may choose to combine the benefit for home care with the benefit for community-based care instead of using the nursing home benefit.

Some policies provide both types of pooled benefits. Other policies provide one or the other.

What Services Are Covered

It is important that you understand what services your long-term care insurance policy covers and how it covers the many types of long-term care services you might need to use. Policies may cover the following:

- nursing home care
- home health care
- respite care
- hospice care
- personal care in your home

- services in assisted living facilities
- services in adult day care centers
- services in other community facilities

There are several ways policies may cover home health care. Some long-term care insurance policies only pay for care in your home from licensed home health agencies. Some also will pay for care from licensed health care providers not from a licensed agency. These include licensed practical nurses; occupational, speech, or physical therapists; or licensed home health care aides. Other policies may pay for services from home health care aides who may not be licensed or are not from licensed agencies. Home health care aides help with personal care. You may find a policy that pays for homemaker or chore worker services. This type of benefit, though not available in all policies, would pay for someone to come to your home to cook meals and run errands. Generally, adding home care benefits to a policy also adds to the cost of the policy.

NOTE: Some policies pay benefits to family members who give care in the home.

Where Services Are Covered

You should know what types of facilities are covered by your long-term care insurance policy. If you're not in the right type of facility, the insurance company can refuse to pay for eligible services. New kinds of facilities may be developed in the future and it is important to know whether your policy will cover them.

Some policies may pay for care in *any* state-licensed facility. Others only pay for care in *some* state-licensed facilities, such as a licensed nursing facility. Still others list the types of facilities where services will not be covered, which may include state licensed facilities. (For example, some places that care for elderly people are referred to as homes for the aged, rest homes, and personal care homes, and are often not covered by long-term care policies). Some policies may list specific points about the kinds of facilities they will cover. Some will say the facilities must care for a certain number of patients or give a certain kind of care. When shopping for a long-term care policy, check these points carefully and compare the types of services and facilities covered in the policy. Also, be aware that many states, companies and policies define assisted living facilities differently. Policies that cover assisted living facilities in one state may not cover services provided in an assisted living facility in another state. Before you move or retire to another state, ask if your policy covers the types of services and facilities available in your new state. Also, if your policy lists kinds of facilities, be sure to check if your policy requires the facility to have a license or certification from a government agency.

NOTE: If you do *not* reside in the kind of facility specified by your policy, the insurance company may not pay for the services you require.

What Services Are Not Covered (Exclusions and Limitations)

Most long-term care insurance policies usually do not pay benefits for:

- a mental or nervous disorder or disease, other than Alzheimer's disease or other **dementia**;
- alcohol or drug addiction;
- illness or injury caused by an act of war;
- treatment the government has provided in a government facility or already paid for; or
- attempted suicide or intentionally self-inflicted injuries.

NOTE: In most states, regulations require insurance companies to pay for covered services for Alzheimer's disease that may develop after a policy is issued. Ask your state insurance department if this applies in your state. Nearly all policies specifically say they will cover Alzheimer's disease. Read about Alzheimer's disease and eligibility for benefits in the section on benefit triggers on page 253.

NOTE: Many policies exclude or limit coverage for care outside of the United States.

How Much Coverage You Will Have

The policy or certificate may state the amount of coverage in one of several ways. A policy may pay different amounts for different types of long-term care services. Be sure you understand how much coverage you will have and how it will cover long-term care services you receive.

Maximum Benefit Limit. Most policies limit the total benefit they will pay over the life of the policy, but a few don't. Some policies state the maximum benefit limit in years (one, two, three, or more, or even lifetime). Others write the policy maximum benefit limit as a total dollar amount. Policies often use words like "total lifetime benefit," "maximum lifetime benefit," or "total plan benefit" to describe their maximum benefit limit. When you look at a policy or certificate be sure to check the total amount of coverage. In most states, the minimum benefit period is one year. Most nursing home stays are short, but illnesses that go on for several years could mean long nursing home stays. You will have to decide if you want protection for very long stays. Policies with longer maximum benefit periods cost more. Read your long-term care insurance policy carefully to learn what the benefit period is.

Daily/Weekly/Monthly Benefit Limit. Policies normally pay benefits by the day, week or month. For example, in an expense-incurred plan, a policy might pay a daily nursing home benefit of up to $200 per day or $6,000 per month, and a weekly home care benefit of up to $1,400 per week. Some policies will pay one time for single events, such as installing a home medical alert system.

When you buy a policy, insurance companies let you choose a benefit amount (usually $50 to $350 a day, $350 to $2,450 a week, or $1,500 to $10,500 a month) for care in a nursing home. If a policy covers home care, the benefit is usually a portion of the benefit for nursing home care (e.g., 50% or 75%), although a growing number of policies pay the same benefit amounts for care at home as in a facility. Often, you can select the home care benefit amount that you prefer. It is important to know how much skilled nursing homes, assisted living facilities, and home health care agencies charge for their services *before* you choose the benefit amounts in your long-term care insurance policy. Check the facilities in the area where you think you may be receiving care, whether they are local, near a grown child, or in a new place where you may retire. The worksheet on page 284 can help you track these costs.

When You Are Eligible for Benefits (Benefit Triggers)

The term usually used to describe the way insurance companies decide when to pay benefits is "benefit triggers." This term refers to the criteria and the methods that the insurance company uses to evaluate when you are eligible for benefits, and the conditions you must meet to receive benefits. This is an important part of a long-term care insurance policy. Look at it carefully as you shop. The policy and the outline of coverage usually describe the benefit triggers. Look for a section called "Eligibility for the Payment of Benefits" or simply "Eligibility for Benefits." Different policies may have different benefit triggers. Some states require certain benefit triggers, and the benefit triggers for tax-qualified contracts are also fairly standardized across insurance policies. Check with your state insurance department to find out what your state requires.

NOTE: Companies may use different benefit triggers for home health care coverage than for nursing home care, although most do not do so. If they do, they generally have a more restrictive benefit trigger for nursing home care than for home care.

Types of Benefit Triggers

Activities of Daily Living. The inability to do activities of daily living, or ADLs, is the most common way insurance companies decide when you are eligible for benefits. The ADLs most companies use are **bathing, continence, dressing, eating, toileting** and **transferring**. Typically, a policy pays benefits when you can't do a certain number of the ADLs, such as two of the six or three of the six. The more ADLs you must be unable to do, the harder it will be for you to become eligible for benefits. Federally tax-qualified policies are required to use being unable to do certain ADLs as a benefit trigger. A qualified policy requires that a person be unable to perform at least two of their ADLs to collect benefits. The ADLs that trigger benefits in a tax-qualified policy must come from the list above. These triggers are specified in your policy.

If the policy you're thinking of buying pays benefits when you can't do certain ADLs, be sure you understand what that means. Some policies spell out very clearly what it means to be unable to feed or bathe oneself. Some policies say that you must have someone actually help you do the activities. That's known as hands-on assistance. Specifying hands-on assistance will make it harder to qualify for benefits than if only standby assistance is required. The more clearly a policy describes its requirements, the less confusion you or your family will have when you need to file a claim.

NOTE: The six activities of daily living (ADLs) have been developed through years of research. This research also has shown that bathing is usually the first ADL that a person can't do. While most policies use all six ADLs as benefit triggers, qualifying for benefits from a policy that uses five ADLs may be more difficult if bathing isn't one of the five.

Cognitive Impairment. Most long-term care insurance policies also pay benefits for "**cognitive impairment**." The policy usually pays benefits if you can't pass certain tests of cognitive function.

Coverage of cognitive impairment is especially important if you develop Alzheimer's disease or other dementia. If being unable to do ADLs is the only benefit trigger your policy uses, it may not pay benefits if you have Alzheimer's disease but can still do most of the ADLs on your own. But if your policy also uses a test of your cognitive ability as a benefit trigger, it is more likely to pay benefits if you have Alzheimer's disease. Most states do not allow policies to limit benefits solely because you have Alzheimer's disease.

Doctor Certification of Medical Necessity. Some long-term care insurance policies will pay benefits if your doctor orders or certifies that the care is medically necessary. However, tax qualified policies can't use this benefit trigger.

Prior Hospitalization. Long-term care insurance policies sold in the past required a hospital stay of at least three days before paying benefits. Most companies no longer sell policies that require a hospital stay.

NOTE: Medicare still requires a three-day hospital stay to be eligible for Medicare payment of skilled nursing facility benefits.

When Benefits Start (Elimination Period)

With many policies, your benefits won't start the first day you go to a nursing home or start using home care. Most policies have an **elimination period** (sometimes called a deductible or a waiting period). That means benefits can start 0, 20, 30, 60, 90, or 100 days after you start using long-term care or become disabled. Elimination periods for nursing home and home health care may be different, or there may be a single elimination period that applies to any covered service. How many days you have to wait for benefits to start will depend on the elimination period you pick when you buy your policy. You might be able to choose a policy with a zero-day elimination period, but expect it to cost more.

Some policies calculate the elimination period using calendar days while other policies count only the days on which you receive a covered service. Under the calendar days method, every day of the week would count in determining the elimination period regardless of whether you received any services on those days. Under the days of service method, only days when you receive services will count toward the elimination period. This means if you only receive services three days a week, it will take longer for your benefits to start and it could mean that you have more out of-pocket expenses before your benefits begin. Also, some policies have an elimination period that you only need to satisfy once in your lifetime, while other policies require that you satisfy the elimination period with each "episode of care." Some policies allow you to accumulate non-consecutive days toward satisfying the elimination period and some policies require consecutive days. Make sure you know how the policy defines the elimination period.

During an elimination period, the policy will not pay the cost of long-term care services. You may owe the cost of your care during the elimination period. You may choose to pay a higher premium for a shorter elimination period. If you choose a longer elimination period, you'll pay a lower premium but must pay the cost of your care during the elimination period.

For example, if a nursing home in your area costs $150 a day and your policy has a 30-day elimination period, you'd have to pay $4,500 before your policy starts to pay benefits. A policy with a 60-day elimination period would mean you'd have to pay $9,000 of your own money, while a policy with a 90-day elimination period would mean you'd have to pay $13,500 of your own money.

If you only need care for a short time and your policy has a long elimination period, your policy may not pay any benefits. If, for example, your policy had a 100-day elimination period, and you received long-term care services for only 60 days, you would not receive any benefits from your policy.

On the other hand, if you can afford to pay for long-term care services for a short time, a longer elimination period might be right for you. It would protect you if you need extended care and also keep the cost of your insurance down.

You may also want to think about how the policy pays if you have a repeat stay in a nursing home. Some policies count the second stay as part of the first one as long as you leave and then go back within 30, 90 or 180 days. Find out if the insurance company requires another elimination period for a second stay. Some policies only require you to meet the elimination period once per lifetime.

What Happens When Long-Term Care Costs Rise (Inflation Protection)?

Inflation protection can be one of the most important additions you can make to a long-term care insurance policy. Inflation protection increases the premium. However, unless your benefits increase over time, years from now you may find that they haven't kept up with the rising cost of long-term care. The cost of nursing home care has been rising at an annual rate of 5% for the past several years.[16] This means that a nursing home that cost $150 a day in 2000 will cost $398 a day in 20 years, if inflation is 5% a year. Obviously, the younger you are when you buy a policy, the more important it is for you to think about adding inflation protection.

You can usually buy inflation protection in one of two ways: automatically or by special offer.

Automatic Inflation Protection. The first way automatically increases your benefits each year. Generally, there would be no increase in premium when the benefit is automatically increased. Policies that increase benefits for inflation automatically may use simple or compound rates. Either way, the daily benefit increases each year by a fixed percentage, usually 5%, for the life of the policy or for a certain period, usually 10 or 20 years.

The dollar amount of the increase depends on whether the inflation adjustment is "simple" or "compound." If the inflation increase is simple, the benefit increases by the same dollar amount each year. If the increase is compounded, the dollar amount of the benefit increase goes up each year. For example, a $100 daily benefit that increases by a simple 5% a year will go up $5 a year and be $200 a day in 20 years. If the increase is compounded, the annual increase will be higher each year and the $100 daily benefit will be $265 a day in 20 years.

Automatic inflation increases that are compounded are a good idea but not all policies offer them. Some states now require policies to offer compound inflation increases. *Check with your state insurance department to find out if this applies in your state.* All individual and some group tax-qualified policies must offer compound inflation increases as an option. Compounding can make a big difference in the size of your benefit.

Special Offer or Non-Automatic Inflation Protection. The second way to buy inflation protection lets you choose to increase your benefits periodically, such as every two or three years. With a periodic increase option, you usually don't have to show proof of good health, if you regularly use the option. Your premium will increase if you increase your benefits. How much it increases depends on your age at the time and on the amount of additional benefit you want to buy. Buying more benefits every few years may help you afford the cost of the additional coverage. If you turn down the option to increase your benefit one year, you may not get the chance again. If you get the chance later, you may have to prove good health, or it may cost you more money. If you don't accept the offer, you need to check your policy to see how it will affect future offers. Some policies continue the inflation offers while you are receiving benefits, but most do not. So check your policy carefully before you buy.

The following charts and graphs illustrate the effects of inflation in two different formats.

Effect of Inflation on Daily Rates for Nursing Home Care

| Rate of Inflation | Compound Interest | | | | |
	2000	2005	2010	2015	2020
5%	$150	$191	$244	$312	$398
6%	$150	$201	$269	$359	$481
7%	$150	$210	$295	$414	$580
8%	$150	$220	$324	$476	$699
Rate of Inflation	Simple Interest				
	2000	2005	2010	2015	2020
5%	$150	$188	$225	$263	$300
6%	$150	$195	$240	$285	$330
7%	$150	$203	$255	$308	$360
8%	$150	$210	$270	$330	$390

The chart is for demonstration purposes only. It shows inflation increases over a 20-year period.

Effect of Inflation on Daily Rates for Nursing Home Care

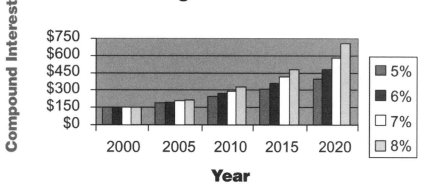

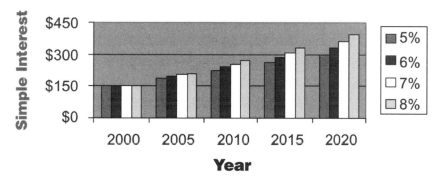

The graphs are for demonstration purposes only. They show compound and simple inflation increases over a 20-year period.

NOTE: Most states have adopted regulations that require companies to offer inflation protection. It's up to you to decide whether to buy the coverage. If you decide not to take the protection, you may be asked to sign a statement saying you didn't want it. Be sure you know what you're signing.

Additional Benefits

Third Party Notice. This benefit lets you name someone who the insurance company would contact if your coverage is about to end because you forgot to pay the premium. Sometimes people with cognitive impairments forget to pay the premium and lose their coverage when they need it the most. You can choose a relative, friend, or a professional (a lawyer or accountant, for example) as your third party. After the company contacts the person you choose, he or she would have some time to arrange for payment of the overdue premium. You can usually name a contact person without paying extra. Some states require insurance companies to give you the chance to name a contact and to update your list of contacts from time to time. You may be required to sign a waiver if you choose not to name anyone to be contacted if the policy is about to lapse.

Other Long-Term Care Insurance Policy Options You Might Choose

You can probably choose other policy features, but keep in mind that not all insurers offer all of the policy options. Each may add to the cost of your policy. Ask your insurer what features increase your policy's cost.

Waiver of Premium. Many policies automatically include this feature, but some may only offer it as an additional optional benefit. Premium waiver lets you stop paying the premium once you are eligible for benefits and the insurance company has started to pay benefits. Some companies waive the premium as soon as they make the first benefit payment. Others wait until you have received benefits for 60 to 90 days.

Restoration of Benefits. This option gives you a way to keep the maximum amount of your original benefit even after your policy has paid you benefits. With this option, if you fully recover after a prior disability and go for a stated period without needing or receiving more long-term care services, your benefit goes back to the amount you first bought. For example, assume your policy paid you $5,000 in long-term care benefits out of a policy maximum of $75,000. You would have $70,000 in benefits left. With a restoration of benefits option, if you fully recovered and didn't need or use any long-term care services for a specified time (usually 6 months), your maximum benefit would go back to the original $75,000.

Premium Refund at Death. This benefit pays to your estate any premiums you paid minus any benefits the company paid. To get a refund at death, you must have paid premiums for a certain number of years. Some companies refund premiums only if the policyholder dies before a certain age, usually 65 or 75. The premium refund option may also add to the cost of a policy.

Downgrades. While it may not always appear in the contract, most insurers let policyholders reduce their coverage if they have trouble paying the premium. When you downgrade to a less comprehensive policy, you will pay a lower premium, usually based on your age at the time your purchased your original policy. This may allow you to keep the policy in force instead of dropping it.

What Happens If You Can't Afford the Premiums Anymore?

Nonforfeiture Benefits. If, for whatever reason, you drop your coverage and you have a nonforfeiture benefit in your policy, you will receive some benefit value for the money you've paid into the policy. Without this type of benefit, you get nothing even if you've paid premiums for 10 or 20 years before dropping the policy.

Some states may require insurance companies to offer long-term care insurance policies with a written offer of nonforfeiture benefit. In this case, you may be given benefit options with different premium costs including **reduced paid-up policies, shortened benefit period policies** and **extended term policies.** Under these benefit options, when you stop paying your premiums, the company gives you a **paid-up policy.** Depending on the option you chose, your paid-up policy either will have the same benefit period but with a lower daily benefit (reduced paid-up policy) or will have the same daily benefit but with a shorter benefit period (shortened benefit period policy or extended term policy). Under all of these options, the level of benefits you will receive depends on how long you paid premiums and the amount of premiums you have paid. Since it's paid-up, you won't owe any more premiums.

Other insurers may offer a "return of premium" nonforfeiture benefit. They pay back to you all or part of the premiums that you paid in if you drop your policy after a certain number of years. This is generally the most expensive type of nonforfeiture benefit. A nonforfeiture benefit can add roughly 10% to 100% (and sometimes more) to a policy's cost. How much it adds depends on such things as your age at the time you bought the policy, the type of nonforfeiture benefit, and whether the policy has inflation protection.

You have the option to add a nonforfeiture benefit if you're buying a tax-qualified policy. The "return of premium" nonforfeiture benefit, the "reduced paid-up policy" and the "shortened benefit period policy" may be available options under a tax-qualified policy if you drop the policy. You should consult a tax advisor to see if adding a nonforfeiture benefit would be good for you.

Contingent Nonforfeiture. In some states, if you don't accept the offer of a nonforfeiture benefit, a company is required to provide a "contingent benefit upon lapse." This means that when your premiums increase to a certain level (based on a table of increases), the "contingent benefit upon lapse" will take effect. For example, if you bought the policy at age 70 and did *not* accept the insurance company's offer of a nonforfeiture benefit, if the premium rises to 40% more than the original premium you will be offered the opportunity to accept one of the "contingent benefits upon lapse." The benefits offered are: 1) a reduction in the benefits provided by the current policy so that premium costs stay the same; *or* 2) a conversion of the policy to paid-up status with a shorter benefit period. You may also choose to keep your policy and continue to pay the higher premium.

» Will Your Health Affect Your Ability to Buy a Policy?

Companies that sell long-term care insurance medically "underwrite" their coverage. They look at your health and health history before they decide to issue a policy. You may be able to buy coverage through an employer or another type of group without any health underwriting or with more relaxed underwriting. Insurance companies' underwriting practices affect the premiums they charge you now and in the future. Some companies do what is known as "short-form" underwriting. They ask you to answer a few questions on the insurance application about your health. For example, they may want to know if you have been in a nursing home or received care at home in the last 12 months.

Sometimes companies don't check your medical record until you file a claim. Then they may try to refuse to pay you benefits because of information found in your medical record after you file your claim. This practice is called "post-claims underwriting." It is illegal in many states. Companies that thoroughly check your health before selling you a policy aren't as likely to do post-claims underwriting.

Some companies do more underwriting. They may ask more questions, look at your current medical records, and ask your doctor for a statement about your health. These companies may insure fewer people with health problems. If you have certain conditions that are likely to mean you'll soon need long-term care (Parkinson's disease, for example), you probably can't buy coverage from these companies.

No matter how the company underwrites, you must answer certain questions that the company uses to decide if it will insure you. When you fill out your application, be sure to answer all questions correctly and completely. A company depends on the information you put on your application. If the information is wrong, an insurance company may decide to rescind your policy and return the premiums you have paid. It can usually do this within two years after you buy the policy. Most states require the insurance company to give you a copy of your application when it delivers the policy. At this time, you can review your answers again. You should keep this copy of the application with your insurance papers.

» What Happens If You Have Pre-Existing Conditions?

A long-term care insurance policy usually defines a **pre-existing condition** as one for which you received medical advice or treatment or had symptoms within a certain period before you applied for the policy. Some companies look further back in time than others. That may be important to you if you have a pre-existing condition. A company that learns you didn't tell it about a pre-existing condition on your application might not pay for treatment related to that condition and might even cancel your coverage. A company can usually do this within two years after you buy the policy, or in some cases later, if you intentionally mislead the insurer.

Many companies will sell a policy to someone with a pre-existing condition. However, the company may not pay benefits for long-term care related to that condition for a period after the policy goes into effect, usually six months. Some companies have longer pre-existing condition periods; others have none.

» Can You Renew Your Long-Term Care Insurance Policy?

In most states, long-term care insurance policies sold today must be guaranteed renewable. When a policy is **guaranteed renewable**, it means that the insurance company guarantees you a chance to renew the policy. It does not mean that it guarantees you a chance to renew at the same premium. Your premium may go up over time as your company pays more claims and more expensive claims.

Insurance companies can raise the premiums on their policies but only if they increase the premiums on all policies that are the same in that state. *No individual can be singled out for a rate increase,* no matter how many claims have been filed. In some states, the premium can't increase just because you are older.

If you bought a policy in a group setting and you leave the group, you may be able to keep your group coverage or convert it to an individual policy but you may pay more. *You can ask your state insurance department if your state requires this option.*

» How Much Do Long-Term Care Insurance Policies Cost?

A long-term care insurance policy can be expensive. Be sure you can pay the premiums and still afford your other health insurance and other expenses.

Premiums will vary based on a variety of factors. These factors include your age and health when you buy a policy and the level of coverage, benefits, and options you select for your policy. If you buy a policy with a large daily benefit, a longer maximum benefit period, or a home health care benefit, it will cost you more. Inflation protection and nonforfeiture benefits can increase premiums for long-term care substantially. Inflation protection can add 25% to 40% to the premium. Nonforfeiture benefits can add 10% to 100% to the premium, as noted on page 261. In fact, either of these options can easily double your premium depending on your age when you buy a policy.

The older you are when you buy long-term care insurance, the higher your premiums will be since it's more likely you will need long-term care services. (See "Who May Need Long-Term Care" on page 239.) If you buy at a younger age, your premiums will be lower, but you will pay premiums for a longer period of time. Recent studies have found the average age of purchasers was age 65 in the individual market and age 43 in the employer-sponsored market.[17]

Here is an example of how much premiums can fluctuate based on your age and your coverage options[18]:

The average annual premiums for basic long-term care insurance ($100 daily benefit amount, four years of coverage, and a 20-day elimination period) that does not include a 5% compound inflation protection option or a nonforfeiture benefits option were:

- $300 for a 40-year old;
- $409 for a 50-year old;
- $1,002 for a 65-year old; and
- $4,166 for a 79-year old.

The average annual premiums for the same policy with the 5% compound inflation protection option but no nonforfeiture benefit option were:

- $649 for a 40-year old;
- $881 for a 50-year old;
- $1,802 for a 65-year old; and
- $5,895 for a 79-year old.

The average annual premiums for the same policy with the nonforfeiture benefits option but no inflation protection were:

- $382 for a 40-year old;
- $506 for a 50-year old;
- $1,196 for a 65-year old; and
- $5,067 for a 79-year old.

The average annual premiums for the same policy with both the 5% compound inflation protection option and the nonforfeiture benefits option were:

- $798 for a 40-year old;
- $1,087 for a 50-year old;
- $2,130 for a 65-year old; and
- $7,000 for a 79-year old.

Remember, your actual premium may be very different if it's based on other factors.

Another issue to keep in mind is that long-term care insurance policies may not cover the entire cost of your care. For example, your policy may cover $110 per day in a nursing home, but the total cost of care may be $150 per day. You must pay the difference. Remember, medications and therapies will increase your total daily costs for care. The costs of long-term care in your state should influence the amount of coverage you buy and the premiums you will pay. (See "How Much Does Long-Term Care Cost?" on page 235.)

When you buy a long-term care policy, think about how much your income is and how much you could afford to spend on a long-term care insurance policy now. Also try to think about what your future income and living expenses are likely to be and how much premium you can pay then. If you don't expect your income to increase, it probably isn't a good idea to buy a policy if you can barely afford the premium now.

You also need to think about whether you could afford a rate increase on your policy some time in the future. Remember, while a company cannot raise your rates based on your age or health, the company can raise the rates for an entire class of policies. Some states have laws that limit rate increases. *Check with your insurance department to learn how your state regulates rate increases.* A directory of state insurance departments begins on page 301. Again, it probably isn't a good idea to buy a policy if you can barely afford the premium now.

NOTE: Don't be misled by the term "level premium." You may be told that your long-term care insurance premium is "level". That doesn't mean that it will never increase. Except for **whole life insurance** policies and **noncancellable policies** or riders, companies can't guarantee premiums will never increase. Many states have adopted regulations that don't let insurance companies use the word "level" to sell guaranteed renewable policies. *Companies must tell consumers that premiums may go up.* Look for that information on the outline of coverage and the policy's face page when you shop.

» What Options Do I Have to Pay the Premiums on the Policy?

If you decide you can afford to buy a long-term care insurance policy, there are two main ways in which you may be able to pay your premiums — the **continuous payment option** and the **limited payment option**.

Under the continuous payment option, you would pay the premiums on your policy until you trigger your benefits, traditionally on a monthly, quarterly, semi-annual or annual basis. The policy is not cancelable except in the event of nonpayment of premiums; however, the insurance company can increase premiums on an entire class of policies. Premiums are usually the lowest available under this payment option.

In addition to the continuous payment option, you may be able to pay your premiums under a limited payment option. Under this option, you would pay premiums for a set time period using one of the following ways:

- Single pay. This allows you to make one lump-sum payment.
- Ten-pay and 20-pay. This allows you to complete payment of your premiums in 10 or 20 years, depending on the option you chose. You might choose this option if your income will be lower in 10 or 20 years.
- Pay-to-65. You pay higher than usual premiums, but payments end when you reach age 65.

After the last premium payment, neither you nor the company can cancel the policy. Policies with the limited payment option are more expensive than continuous payment policies, because your premium is set at a higher rate than it would have been had you paid over a longer period of time. In addition, unless the contract fixes your premium for the pay period, it could increase. However, the guaranteed fixed payment and the no-cancel features make limited payment premiums attractive to some clients. You should consult your tax adviser for information on the tax treatment of accelerated premium payments.

It is important to note that not all of these payment options are offered by all companies or are available in all states. Check with the insurance company to see what payment options it offers. *Also check with your state insurance department to find out what options your state allows.* A directory of state insurance departments begins on page 301.

» If You Already Own a Policy, Should You Switch Plans or Upgrade the Coverage You Have Now?

Before you switch to a new long-term care insurance policy, make sure it is better than the one you already have. Even if your agent now works for another company, think carefully before making any changes. First check to see if you can upgrade the coverage on your current policy. If not, you may replace your current policy with a different one that gives you more benefits, or even choose a second policy. Be sure to discuss any change in your coverage with your financial advisor.

If you decide to switch to a new long-term care insurance policy, make sure the new company has accepted your application and issued the new policy before you cancel the old one. When you cancel a policy in the middle of its term, many companies will not give back any premiums you have paid. If you switch policies, new restrictions on pre-existing conditions may apply. You may not have coverage for some conditions for a certain period.

Switching may be right for you if your old policy requires you to stay in the hospital or to receive other types of care before it pays benefits. Before you decide to change, though, make sure you are in good health and can qualify for another policy. If you bought a policy when you were younger, you might ask the insurance company if you can improve it. For example, you might add inflation protection or take off the requirement that you stay in the hospital. It might cost less to improve a policy you have now than to buy a new one.

» What Shopping Tips Should You Keep in Mind?

Here are some points to keep in mind as you shop.

Ask questions.

If you have questions about the agent, the insurance company, or the policy, *contact your state insurance department or insurance counseling program.* (A directory starts on page 301.) Make sure the company is reputable and is licensed to sell long-term care insurance policies in your state.

Check with several companies and agents.

Contacting several companies (and agents) before you buy is wise. Be sure to compare benefits, the types of facilities you have to be in to get coverage, the limits on your coverage, what's excluded, and, of course, the premium. (Policies that have the same coverage and benefits may not cost the same.)

Check out the companies' rate increase histories.

Ask companies about their rate increase histories and whether they have increased the rates on the long-term care insurance policies that they sell. Ask to see a company's personal worksheet that includes this information.

Some state Insurance Commissioners annually prepare a consumer rate guide for long-term care insurance. These guides may include an overview of long-term care insurance, a list of companies selling long-term care insurance in your state, the types of benefits and policies you can buy (both as an individual and as a member of a group), and a rate history of each company that sells long-term care insurance in your state. Some guides even include examples of different coverage types and combinations and provide rates to assist consumers in comparing policies. *Contact your state insurance department or insurance counseling program for this information.* A list of insurance departments and counseling programs starts on page 301.

Take your time and compare outlines of coverage.

Never let anyone pressure or scare you into making a quick decision. Don't buy a policy the first time you see an agent. Ask for an outline of coverage. It outlines the policy's benefits and points out important features. Compare outlines of coverage for several policies and make sure the outlines are similar (if not the same) when comparing premiums. In most states the agent must leave an outline of coverage when he or she first contacts you.

Understand the policies.

Make sure you know what the policy covers and what it doesn't. If you have any questions, call the insurance company before you buy.

If you receive any information that confuses you or is different from the information in the company literature, don't hesitate to call or write the company to ask your questions. Don't trust any sales presentation or literature that claims you have only one chance to buy a policy.

Some companies sell their policies through agents, and others may sell their policies through the mail, skipping agents entirely. No matter how you buy your policy, check with the company if you don't understand how the policy works.

Talk about the policy with a friend or relative. *You may also want to contact your state insurance department or insurance counseling program.* A list of insurance departments and counseling programs starts on page 301.

Don't be misled by advertising.

Most celebrity endorsers are professional actors paid to advertise. They are not insurance experts.

Medicare does not endorse or sell long-term care insurance policies. Be wary of any advertising that suggests Medicare is involved.

Don't trust cards you get in the mail that look like official government documents until you check with the government agency identified on the card. Insurance companies or agents trying to find buyers may have sent them. Be careful if anyone asks you questions over the telephone about Medicare or your insurance. They may sell any information you give to long-term care insurance marketers, who might call you, come to your home, or try to sell you insurance by mail.

Don't buy more coverage than you need.

You don't have to buy more than one policy to get enough coverage. One good policy is enough. Also, don't buy more insurance than you need. For example, buying a policy with a $500 daily benefit in order to prepare for inflation is not necessary. You should choose the daily benefit that matches the cost of long-term care. For more information, reread the section "If You Already Own a Policy, Should You Switch Plans or Upgrade the Coverage You Have Now?" on page 268. Be sure to discuss any change in your coverage with your financial advisor.

Be sure you accurately complete your application.

Don't be misled by long-term care insurance marketers who say your medical history isn't important—it is! Give correct information. If an agent fills out the application for you, don't sign it until you have read it. Make sure that all of the medical information is accurate and complete. If it isn't and the company used that information to decide whether to insure you, it can refuse to pay your claims and can even cancel your policy.

Never pay in cash.

Use a check or an electronic bank draft made payable to the insurance company.

Be sure to get the name, address, and telephone number of the agent and the company.

Get a local or toll-free number for both the agent and the company.

If you don't get your policy within 60 days, contact the company or agent.

You have a right to expect prompt delivery of your policy. When you get it, keep it somewhere you can easily find it. Tell a trusted friend or relative where it is.

Be sure you look at your policy during the free-look period.

If you decide you don't want the policy soon after you bought it, you can cancel it and get your money back. You must tell the company you don't want the policy within a certain number of days after you get it. How many days you have depends on the "free-look" period. In some states the insurance company must tell you about the free-look period on the cover page of the policy. In most states you have 30 days to cancel, but in some you have less time. *Check with your state insurance department to find out how long the free-look period is in your state.* If you want to cancel:

■ Keep the envelope the policy was mailed in. Or ask the agent for a signed delivery receipt when he or she hands you the policy.

■ Send the policy to the insurance company along with a short letter asking for a refund.

■ Send both the policy and the letter by certified mail. Keep the mailing receipt.

■ Keep a copy of all letters.

It usually takes four to six weeks to get your refund.

Read the policy again and make sure it gives you the coverage you want.

Check the policy to see if the benefits and the premiums are what you expected. If you have any questions, call the agent or company right away.

Also, reread the application you signed. It is part of the policy. If it's not filled out correctly, contact the agent or company right away. You may want to fill out Worksheet 3 on page 292.

Think about having the premium automatically taken out of your bank account.

Automatic withdrawal may mean that you won't lose your coverage if an illness makes you forget to pay your premium. If you decide not to renew your policy, be sure you tell the bank to stop the automatic withdrawals.

Check on the financial stability of the company you're thinking about buying from.

Several insurer rating services analyze the financial strength of insurance companies. The ratings can show you how some analysts see the financial health of individual insurance companies. Different rating services use different rating scales. Be sure to find out how the agency labels its highest ratings and the meaning of the ratings for the companies you are considering.

You can get ratings from some insurer rating services for free at most public libraries. Or you can call the services directly at the numbers listed below. (Note that calls to a "900" number will mean an extra charge on your telephone bill.) And now you can get information from these services on the Internet.

Rating Agencies

A.M. Best Company
(900) 439-2200 (billed to telephone) or (800) 424-BEST (charged to credit card) or on the Internet at *http://www.ambest.com*

Fitch IBCA, Duff & Phelps, Inc.
(212) 908-0800 or on the Internet at *http://www.bankwatch.com*

Moody's Investor Service, Inc.
(212) 553-0377 or on the Internet at *http://www.moodys.com*

Standard & Poor's Insurance Rating Services

(212) 488-2000 or on the Internet at *http://www.standardandpoors.com*

Weiss Ratings, Inc.

(800) 289-9222 or on the Internet at *http://www.WeissRatings.com*

REFERENCES

1 U.S. Department of Labor, Bureau of Labor Statistics, 2001.

2 National Center for Assisted Living. "Facts and Trends: The Assisted Living Sourcebook, 2001."

3 U.S. Department of Labor, Bureau of Labor Statistics, 2001.

4 U.S. Department of Labor, 2000. Medicare will pay less than 10 percent of nursing home costs.

5 Centers for Medicaid and Medicare Services, *Medicare & You 2002 Guide*.

6 Centers for Medicare and Medicaid Services. *2002 Guide to Health Insurance for People with Medicare*, page 25.

7 CMS National Health Expenditures, January 2002. Medicaid pays for 48% of all nursing home care.

8 Omnibus Budget Reconciliation Act of 1993 (OBRA). OBRA requires each state to have an "Estate Recovery Program," which is designed to recover the costs of Medicaid-paid benefits from that person's estate or the estate of his or her spouse. If you are age 55 or over and receive Medicaid benefits for nursing home care and related services, OBRA requires that states recover the paid benefits in an amount equal to the total of the assistance provided from your estate. This could include your home and any other property that otherwise would be passed to your heirs.

9 *The Older Population, A Profile of Older Americans: 2001*, Administration on Aging. Information in profile based on data gathered in the 2000 U.S. Census.

10 National Academy on Aging, 1997.

11 Stillman and Lubitz, "Medical Care" 40 (10):965-967 (2002).

12 Stillman and Lubitz, "Medical Care" 40 (10):965-967 (2002).

13 Health Insurance Association of America (HIAA) survey. "Research Findings: Long-Term Care Insurance in 1998-1999" February 2002, pages 3, 5, 13, 17, 27. The employer-sponsored market contributed 25% of the sales in 1999. By the end of 1999, more than 1 million policies had been sold through more than 3,200 employers. This represents a 35% average annual growth rate. There were more than 770 employer-sponsored plans introduced in 1999 alone.

14 Members of the federal family can obtain information on this program from the United States Office of Personnel Management by calling the toll-free number 1-800-582-3337 or by accessing the website at http://www.opm.gov/insure/ltc/.

15 Internal Revenue Service, Revenue Procedure 97-57.

16 U.S. Department of Labor, Bureau of Labor Statistics, 2000. Data shows that between 1995 and 2001, the average nursing home costs have risen about 5%.

17 Health Insurance Association of America (HIAA) survey. "Research Findings: Long-Term Care Insurance in 1998-1999." February 2002.

18 Health Insurance Association of America (HIAA) survey. "Research Findings: Long-Term Care Insurance in 1998-1999" February 2002. Table 5, p. 26. "Average Annual Premiums for Leading Long-Term Care Insurance Sellers in 1999."

» Glossary

Accelerated Death Benefit—A feature of a life insurance policy that lets you use some of the policy's death benefit prior to death.

Activities of Daily Living (ADLs)—Everyday functions and activities individuals usually do without help. ADLs functions include bathing, continence, dressing, eating, toileting and transferring. Many policies use the inability to do a certain number of ADLs (such as 2 of 6) to decide when to pay benefits.

Adult Day Care—Care provided during the day at a community-based center for adults who need assistance or supervision during the day including help with personal care, but who do not need round-the-clock care.

Alzheimer's Disease—A progressive, degenerative form of dementia that causes severe intellectual deterioration.

Assisted Living Facility—A residential living arrangement that provides individualized personal care and health services for people who require assistance with activities of daily living. The types and sizes of facilities vary; they can range from a small home to a large apartment-style complex. They also vary in the levels of care and services that can be provided. Assisted living facilities offer a way to keep a relatively independent lifestyle for people who don't need the level of care provided by nursing homes.

Bathing—Washing oneself by sponge bath, in either a tub or shower. This activity includes the task of getting into or out of the tub or shower.

Benefit Triggers (Triggers)—Term used by insurance companies to describe the criteria and methods they use to determine when you are eligible to receive benefits.

Benefits—Monetary sum paid or payable to a recipient for which the insurance company has receive the premiums.

Care Management Services—A service in which a professional, typically a nurse or social worker, may arrange, monitor, or coordinate long-term care services (also referred to as care coordination services).

Cash Surrender Value—The amount of money you may be entitled to receive from the insurance company when you terminate a life insurance or annuity policy. The amount of cash value will be determined as stated in the policy.

Chronic Illness—An illness with one or more of the following characteristics: permanency, residual disability, requires rehabilitation training, or requires a long period of supervision, observation, or care.

Chronically Ill—A term used in a tax-qualified long-term care contract to describe a person who needs long-term care either because of an inability to do everyday activities of daily living (ADLs) without help or because of a severe cognitive impairment.

Cognitive Impairment—A deficiency in a person's short- or long-term memory; orientation as to person, place and time; deductive or abstract reasoning; or judgment as it relates to safety awareness.

Community-Based Services—Services designed to help older people stay independent and in their own homes.

Continence—The ability to maintain control of bowel and bladder function; or when unable to maintain control these functions, the ability to perform associated personal hygiene (including caring for catheter or colostomy bag).

Continuing Care Retirement Communities (CCRC)—A retirement complex that offers a broad range of services and levels of care.

Continuous Payment Option—A premium payment option that requires you to pay premiums until you trigger your benefits. Premiums are usually paid on a monthly, quarterly, semi-annual or annual basis. The policy is not cancelable except when premiums aren't paid; however, the insurance company can increase premiums on an entire class of policies. Premiums are usually the lowest available.

Custodial Care (Personal Care)—Care to help individuals meet personal needs such as bathing, dressing, and eating. Someone without professional training may provide care.

Daily Benefit—The amount of insurance benefit in dollars a person chooses to buy for long-term care expenses.

Dementia—Deterioration of intellectual faculties due to a disorder of the brain.

Disability Method—Method of paying benefits that only requires you to meet the benefit eligibility criteria. Once you do, you receive your full daily benefit.

Dressing—Putting on and taking off all items of clothing and any necessary braces, fasteners or artificial limbs.

Eating—Feeding oneself by getting food into the body from a receptacle (such as a plate, cup or table) or by a feeding tube or intravenously.

Elimination Period—A type of deductible; the length of time the individual must pay for covered services before the insurance company will begin to make payments. The longer the elimination period in a policy, the lower the premium. Sometimes also called a "waiting period."

Expense-Incurred Method—Method of paying benefits where the insurance company must decide if you are eligible for benefits and if your claim is for eligible services. Your policy or certificate will pay benefits only when you receive eligible services. Once you have incurred an expense for an eligible service, benefits are paid either to you or your provider. The coverage will pay for the lesser of the expense you incurred or the dollar limit of your policy. Most policies bought today pay benefits using the expense-incurred method.

Extended Term Benefits — Full benefits for a reduced time period, applicable for use during a certain period of time. If not used in a set number of years after the lapse, then you lose it. Once the period has expired, the contract terminates.

Guaranteed Renewable — When a policy cannot be cancelled by an insurance company and must be renewed when it expires unless benefits have been exhausted. The company cannot change the coverage or refuse to renew the coverage for other than nonpayment of premiums (including health conditions and/or marital or employment status). In a guaranteed renewable policy, the insurance company may increase premiums, but only on an entire class of policies, not just on your policy.

Hands-on Assistance — Physical assistance (minimal, moderate, or maximal) without which the individual would not be able to perform the activity of daily living.

Health Insurance Portability and Accountability Act (HIPAA) — Federal health insurance legislation passed in 1996 that allows, under specified conditions, long-term care insurance policies to be qualified for certain tax benefits.

Home for the Aged — A general term for a facility that cares for elderly people. It is often not covered under a long-term care policy.

Home Health Care — Services for occupational, physical, respiratory, or speech therapy or nursing care. Also included are medical, social worker, home health aide, and homemaker services.

Homemaker Services — Household services done by someone other than yourself because you're unable to do them.

Hospice Care—Continuous care provided at home or in a facility with a homelike setting for a terminally ill person. A terminally ill person has a life expectancy of six months or less.

Indemnity Method—Method of paying benefits where the benefit is a set dollar amount and is not based on the specific service received or on the expenses incurred. The insurance company only needs to decide if you are eligible for benefits. Once the company determines you are eligible and you are receiving eligible long-term care services, the insurance company will pay that set amount directly to you up to the limit of the policy.

Inflation Protection—A policy option that provides for increases in benefit levels to help pay for expected increases in the costs of long-term care services.

Lapse—Termination of a policy when a renewal premium is not paid.

Limited Payment Option—A premium payment option in which the person pays premiums for a set time period. After the last premium payment, neither the company nor the person can cancel the policy. These plans are more expensive than continuous payment policies; however, their guaranteed fixed payment and no-cancel features make them attractive to some persons.

Medicaid—A joint federal/state program that pays for health care services for those with low incomes or very high medical bills relative to income and assets.

Medicare—The federal program providing hospital and medical insurance to people aged 65 or older and to certain ill or disabled persons. Benefits for nursing home and home health services are limited.

Medicare Supplement Insurance—A private insurance policy that covers many of the gaps in Medicare coverage (also called Medigap insurance coverage).

National Association of Insurance Commissioners (NAIC)—Membership organization of state insurance commissioners. One of its goals is to promote uniformity of state regulation and legislation related to insurance.

Noncancelable Policies—Insurance contracts that cannot be cancelled by the insurance company and the rates cannot be changed by the insurance company.

Nonforfeiture Benefits—A policy feature that returns at least part of the premiums to you if you cancel your policy or let it lapse.

Nursing Home—A licensed facility that provides general nursing care to those who are chronically ill or unable to take care of daily living needs. May also be referred to as a Long-Term Care Facility.

Paid-up Policy—When you prematurely stop paying your premiums, your insurance policy is deemed to be paid-in-full. You do not pay any more premiums, but the benefits you receive under this policy will be determined based on the amount of premiums you have already paid, not on the level of benefits that you originally purchased.

Partnership Policy—A type of policy that allows you to protect (keep) some of your assets if you apply for Medicaid after using your policy's benefits. Only a few states have these policies.

Personal Care (Custodial Care)—Care to help individuals meet personal needs such as bathing, dressing, and eating. Someone without professional training may provide care.

Personal Care Home—A general term for a facility that cares for elderly people. It is often not covered under a long-term care policy.

Pre-existing Condition—Illnesses or disability for which you were treated or advised within a time period before applying for a life or health insurance policy.

Reduced Paid-up Benefits—A nonforfeiture option that reduces your daily benefit but retains the full benefit period on your policy until death.

For example, you buy a policy for three years of coverage with $150 daily benefit. Then if you let the policy lapse, the daily benefit will be reduced to $100. The exact amount of the reduction depends upon how much premium you have paid on the policy. The benefit period on your policy continues to be three years. Unlike extended term benefits, which must be used in a certain amount of time after the lapse, you can use reduced paid-up benefits at any time after you lapse (until death).

Rescind—When the insurance company voids (cancels) a policy.

Respite Care—Care provided by a third party that relieves family caregivers for a few hours to several days and gives them an occasional break from daily caregiving responsibilities.

Rest Home—A general term for a facility that cares for elderly people. It is often not covered under a long-term care policy.

Rider—Addition to an insurance policy that changes the provisions of the policy.

Shortened Benefit Period—A nonforfeiture option that reduces the benefit period but retains the full daily maximums applicable until death. The period of time for which benefits are paid will be shorter. For example, you buy a policy for three years of coverage with $150 daily benefit, but if you let the policy lapse, the benefit period is reduced to one year, with full daily benefits paid. The exact amount of the reduction depends upon how much premium you have paid on the policy. Unlike extended term benefits, which must be used in a certain amount of time after the lapse, you can use shortened benefits at any time after you let the premium lapse (until death).

Skilled Care—Daily nursing and rehabilitative care that can be performed only by, or under the supervision of, skilled medical personnel. This care is usually needed 24 hours a day, must be ordered by a physician, and must follow a plan of care. Individuals usually get skilled care in a nursing home but may also receive it in other places.

Spend Down—A requirement that an individual use up most of his or her income and assets to meet Medicaid eligibility requirements.

Stand-by Assistance—Caregiver stays close the individual to watch over the individual and to provide physical assistance if necessary.

State Health Insurance Program—Federally funded program to train volunteers to provide counseling on the insurance needs of senior citizens. See pages 301–310 for a list of State Health Insurance Programs.

Substantial Assistance—Hands-on or stand-by help required to do ADLs.

Substantial Supervision—The presence of person directing and watching over another who has a cognitive impairment.

Tax-Qualified Long-Term Care Insurance Policy—A policy that conforms to certain standards in federal law and offers certain federal tax advantages.

Term Life Insurance—Covers a person for a period of one or more years. It pays a death benefit only if you die during that term. It generally does not build a cash value.

Third Party Notice—A benefit which lets you name someone who the insurance company would notify if your coverage is about to end because the premium hasn't been paid. This can be a relative, friend, or professional such as a lawyer or accountant, for example.

Toileting—Getting to and from the toilet, getting on and off the toilet and performing associated personal hygiene.

Transferring—Moving into and out of a bed, chair or wheelchair.

Triggers (Benefit Triggers)—Term used by insurance companies to describe when to pay benefits.

Underwriting—The process of examining, accepting, or rejecting insurance risks, and classifying those selected, to charge the proper premium for each.

Universal Life Insurance—A kind of flexible policy that lets you vary your premium payments and adjust the face amount of your coverage.

Waiver of Premium—A provision in an insurance policy that relieves the insured of paying the premiums while receiving benefits.

Whole Life Insurance—Policies that build cash value and cover a person for as long as he or she lives if premiums continue to be paid.

» Worksheet 1: Information About the Availability and Cost of Long-Term Care in Your Area

Find out what facilities and services provide long-term care in your area (or in the area where you would be most likely to receive care) and what the costs are for these services. List the information below.

Home Health Agency

Name of one home health agency you might use _____

Name of *another* home health agency you might use _____

Address _____

Address _____

Phone number _____

Phone number _____

Contact person _____

Contact person _____

Check which types of care are available and list the cost.

☐ Skilled nursing care
   cost/visit $_____

☐ Skilled nursing care
   cost/visit $_____

☐ Home health care
   cost/visit $_____

☐ Home health care
   cost/visit $_____

☐ Personal/custodial care
   cost/visit $_____

☐ Personal/custodial care
   cost/visit $_____

☐ Homemaker services
   cost/visit $_____

☐ Homemaker services
   cost/visit $_____

Nursing Facility

Name of one nursing facility you might use _____

Name of *another* nursing facility you might use _____

Address _____

Address _____

Phone number _____

Phone number _____

Contact person _____

Contact person _____

Check which types of care are available and list the cost.

☐ Skilled nursing care
cost/month $_____

☐ Skilled nursing care
cost/month $_____

☐ Personal/custodial care
cost/month $_____

☐ Personal/custodial care
cost/month $_____

Other Facility

Other facility or service you might use (e.g., adult day care center, assisted living, etc.) _____

Other facility or service you might use (e.g., adult day care center, assisted living, etc.) _____

Address _____

Address _____

Phone number _____

Phone number _____

Contact person _____

Contact person _____

What services are available? _____

What services are available? _____

What are the costs for those services?

What are the costs for those services?

» Worksheet 2: How to Compare Long-Term Care Insurance Policies

Fill in the information below so that you can compare long-term care insurance policies. Most of the information you need is in the outline of coverage provided in the policies you are comparing. Even so, you will need to calculate some information and talk to the agent or a company representative to get the rest.

	Policy 1	Policy 2
Insurance company information		
1. Name of the insurance company's agent.	_____	_____
2. Is the company licensed in your state?	Yes / No	Yes / No
3. Insurance rating service and rating. (Refer to page 273.)	_____	_____

What levels of care are covered by this policy? (Refer to page 249.)

4. Does the policy provide benefits for these levels of care?		
■ skilled nursing care?	Yes / No	Yes / No
■ personal/custodial care?	Yes / No	Yes / No
(In many states, both levels of care are required.)		
5. Does the policy pay for any nursing home stay, no matter what level of care you receive?	Yes / No	Yes / No
■ If not, what levels aren't covered?	_____	_____

Where can you receive care covered under the policy? (Refer to page 250.)

6. Does the policy pay for care in any licensed facility?	Yes / No	Yes / No
■ If not, what doesn't it pay for?	_____	_____
7. Does the policy provide home care benefits for:		
■ skilled nursing care?	Yes / No	Yes / No
■ personal care given by home health aides?	Yes / No	Yes / No

■ homemaker services?	Yes / No	Yes / No
■ other _____?	Yes / No	Yes / No

8. Does the policy pay for care received in:

■ adult day care centers?	Yes / No	Yes / No
■ assisted living facilities?	Yes / No	Yes / No
■ other settings? (list)	_____	_____

How long are benefits paid and what amounts are covered?
(You may be considering a policy that pays benefits on a different basis, so you may have to do some calculations to determine comparable amounts.) (Refer to page 252.)

9. How much will the policy pay per day for:

■ nursing home care?	$_____	$_____
■ assisted living facility care?	$_____	$_____
■ home care?	$_____	$_____

10. Are there limits on the number of days or visits per year for which benefits will be paid?   Yes / No   Yes / No

If yes, what are the limits for:

■ nursing home care?	_____ days	_____ days
■ assisted living facility care?	_____ days	_____ days
■ home care? (days or visits?)	_____	_____

11. What is the length of the benefit period that you are considering?   _____ years   _____ years

12. Are there limits on the amounts the policy will pay during your lifetime?   Yes / No   Yes / No

If yes, what are the limits for:

■ nursing home care?	$_____	$_____
■ assisted living facility care?	$_____	$_____
■ home care? (days or visits?)	$_____	$_____
■ total lifetime limit?	$_____	$_____

How does the policy decide when you are eligible for benefits?
(Refer to page 253.)

13. Which of the "benefit triggers" does the policy use to decide your eligibility for benefits? (It may have more than one.)

- Unable to do activities of daily living (ADLs).   Yes / No   Yes / No

- Cognitive impairment. (older policies may discriminate against Alzheimer's; newer ones don't.)   Yes / No   Yes / No

- Doctor certification of medical necessity.   Yes / No   Yes / No

- Prior hospital stay.   Yes / No   Yes / No

- Bathing is one of the ADLs.   Yes / No   Yes / No

When do benefits start? (Refer to page 255.)

14. How long is the waiting period before benefits begin for:

- nursing home care?   _____ days   _____ days

- assisted living facility care?   _____ days   _____ days

- home health care?   _____ days   _____ days

- waiting period—service days or calendar days?   _____   _____

15. Are the waiting periods for home care cumulative or consecutive?   _____   _____

16. How long will it be before you are covered for a pre-existing condition? (Usually 6 months)   _____ months   _____ months

17. How long will the company look back in your medical history to determine a pre-existing condition? (Usually 6 months)   _____ months   _____ months

Does the policy have inflation protection? (Refer to page 256.)

18. Are the benefits adjusted for inflation?   Yes / No   Yes / No

19. Are you allowed to buy more
coverage? If yes,   Yes / No   Yes / No

   ■ When can you buy more coverage?   _____   _____

   ■ How much can you buy? $_____ $_____

   ■ When can you no longer buy
more coverage?   _____   _____

20. Do the benefits increase automatically? If yes,

   ■ What is the rate of increase?   _____ %   _____ %

   ■ Is it a simple or compound
increase?   _____   _____

   ■ When do automatic increases stop? _____   _____

21. If you buy inflation coverage, what daily benefit
would you receive for nursing home care:

   ■ 5 years from now? $_____ $_____

   ■ 10 years from now? $_____ $_____

Assisted living facility care:

   ■ 5 years from now? $_____ $_____

   ■ 10 years from now? $_____ $_____

Home health care:

   ■ 5 years from now? $_____ $_____

   ■ 10 years from now? $_____ $_____

22. If you buy inflation coverage, what
will your premium be:

   ■ 5 years from now? $_____ $_____

   ■ 10 years from now? $_____ $_____

   ■ 15 years from now? $_____ $_____

What other benefits are covered under the policy?

23. Is there a waiver of premium benefit?
(Refer to page 260.)   Yes / No   Yes / No

   If yes:

   ■ How long do you have to be in a
   nursing home before it begins?   _____   _____

   ■ Does the waiver apply when you re-
   ceive home care?   Yes / No   Yes / No

24. Does the policy have a nonforfeiture
benefit?   Yes / No   Yes / No

   If yes, what kind?
   (Refer to page 261.)   _____   _____

25. Does the policy have a return of pre-
mium benefit? (Refer to page 261.)   Yes / No   Yes / No

26. Does the policy have a death benefit?   Yes / No   Yes / No

   If yes, are there any restrictions before
   the benefit is paid? (Refer to page
   260.)   Yes / No   Yes / No

27. Will the policy cover one person or
two?   One / Two   One / Two

Tax-qualified status

28. Is the policy tax-qualified?
(Refer to page 245.)   Yes / No   Yes / No

What does the policy cost?
(Refer to page 239.)

29. What is the premium excluding all riders?

   ■ monthly $_____ $_____

   ■ yearly $_____ $_____

30. What is the premium if home care is covered?

   ■ monthly $_____ $_____

   ■ yearly $_____ $_____

31. What is the premium if assisted living is covered?

   ■ monthly $_____ $_____

   ■ yearly $_____ $_____

32. What is the premium if you include an inflation rider?

   ■ monthly $_____ $_____

   ■ yearly $_____ $_____

33. What is the premium if you include a nonforfeiture benefit?

   ■ monthly $_____ $_____

   ■ yearly $_____ $_____

34. Is there any discount if you and your
    spouse both buy policies?   Yes / No   Yes / No

   ■ If yes, what is the amount of the
     discount? $_____ $_____

   ■ Do you lose the discount when
     one spouse dies?   Yes / No   Yes / No

35. What is the total annual premium including all riders and discounts?

   ■ total monthly premium $_____ $_____

   ■ total annual premium $_____ $_____

36. When looking at the results of Ques-
    tions 29 through 35, how much do
    you think you are willing to pay in
    premiums? $_____ $_____

» Worksheet 3: Facts About Your Long-Term Care Insurance Policy

For use after you buy a long-term care policy. Fill out this form and put it with your important papers. You may want to make a copy for a friend or a relative.

1. Insurance policy data

    Policy number _____

    Date purchased _____

    Annual premium $ _____

2. Insurance company information

    Name of company _____

    Address _____

    Phone number _____

3. Agent information

    Agent's name _____

    Address _____

    Phone number _____

4. Type of long-term care policy

    _____ Nursing home only   _____ Other

    _____ Facilities only   _____ Tax-qualified

    _____ Home care only

    _____ Comprehensive (nursing home, assisted living, home and community care)

5. How long is the waiting period before benefits begin? _____

6. How do I file a claim? (Check all that apply.)

    _____ I need prior approval.   _____ Contact the company.

    _____ Submit a plan of care.   _____ Doctor notifies the company.

    _____ Assessment by company.   _____ Assessment by care manager.

    _____ Fill out a claim form.

7. How often do I pay premiums?

_____ annually _____ semi-annually _____ other

Specify other: _____

8. The person to be notified if I forget to pay the premium:

Name _____

Address _____

Phone number _____

9. Are my premiums deducted from my bank account? __ Yes __ No

Name of my bank _____

Address _____

Phone number _____

Bank account number _____

10. Where do I keep this long-term care policy? _____

Other information _____

11. Friend or relative who knows where my policy is:

Name _____

Address _____

Phone number _____

» Worksheet 4: Long-Term Care Riders to Life Insurance Policies

The purpose of this worksheet is to help you to evaluate one or more life long-term care insurance policies. Fill out the form so you can compare your options. In addition, you will want to fill out Worksheet 2 regarding the long-term care benefits provided by the policy.

	Policy 1	Policy 2
Insurance company information		
1. Name of the insurance company's agent	_____	_____
2. Is the company licensed in your state?	Yes / No	Yes / No
3. Insurance rating service and rating (Refer to page 273.)	_____	_____
Policy information		
4. What kind of life insurance policy is it?		
Whole life insurance	Yes / No	Yes / No
Universal life insurance	Yes / No	Yes / No
Term life insurance	Yes / No	Yes / No
5. What is the policy's premium?	$_____	$_____
6. How often is the premium paid?		
One time / single premium	Yes / No	Yes / No
Annually for life	Yes / No	Yes / No
Annually for 10 years only	Yes / No	Yes / No
Annually for 20 years only	Yes / No	Yes / No
Other	Yes / No	Yes / No
7. Is there a separate premium for the long-term care benefit provided by the life insurance policy?	Yes / No	Yes / No
If not, how is the premium paid?		
■ Included in life insurance premium?	Yes / No	Yes / No
■ Deducted from the cash value of the life insurance policy?	Yes / No	Yes / No

8. How many people will the policy
   cover?   _____   _____

9. Will the payment of long-term care
   benefits decrease the death benefit
   and cash value of the policy?   Yes / No   Yes / No

10. Will an outstanding loan affect the
    long-term care benefits?   Yes / No   Yes / No

11. Did you receive an illustration of guar-
    anteed values?   Yes / No   Yes / No

    If yes, do the policy values equal zero
    at some age on a guaranteed or mid-
    point basis?   Yes / No   Yes / No

    If so, at what age?   _____   _____

» Long-Term Care Insurance Personal Worksheet

People buy long-term care insurance for many reasons. Some don't want to use their own assets to pay for long-term care. Some buy insurance to make sure they can choose the type of care they get. Others don't want their family to have to pay for care or don't want to go on Medicaid. But long-term care insurance may be expensive, and may not be right for everyone.

By state law, the insurance company must fill out part of the information on this worksheet and *ask* you to fill out the rest to help you and the company decide if you should buy this policy.

Premium Information

Policy form numbers _____
The premium for the coverage you are considering will be [$_____ per month, or $_____ per year] [a one-time single premium of $_____].

Type of Policy

(noncancellable/guaranteed renewable): _____

The Company's Right to Increase Premiums:

[The company cannot raise your rates on this policy.] [The company has a right to increase premiums on this policy form in the future, provided it raises rates for all policies in the same class in this state.] [Insurers shall use appropriate bracketed statement. Rate guarantees shall not be shown on this form.]

Rate Increase History

The company has sold long-term care insurance since [year] and has sold this policy since [year].

[The company has never raised its rates for any long-term care policy it has sold in this state or any other state.] [The company has not raised its rates for this policy form or similar policy forms in this state or any other state in the last 10 years.] [The company has raised its premium rates on this policy form or similar policy forms in the last 10 years. Following is a summary of the rate increases.]

Drafting Note: A company may use the first bracketed sentence above only if it has never increased rates under any prior policy forms in this state or any other state. The issuer shall list each premium increase it has instituted on this or similar policy forms in this state or any other state during the last 10 years. The list shall provide the policy form, the calendar years the form was available for sale, and the calendar year and the amount (percentage) of each increase. The insurer shall provide minimum and maximum percentages if the rate increase is variable by rating characteristics. The insurer may provide, in a fair manner, additional explanatory information as appropriate.

Questions Related to Your Income

How will you pay each year's premium?

☐ From my income   ☐ From my savings/investments
☐ My family will pay.

[Have you considered whether you could afford to keep this policy if the premiums went up, for example, by 20%?]

Drafting Note: The issuer is not required to use the bracketed sentence if the policy is fully paid up or is a noncancellable policy.

What is your annual income? (check one)

☐ Under $10,000   ☐ $[10–20,000]

☐ $[20–30,000]   ☐ $[30–50,000]   ☐ Over $50,000

Drafting Note: The issuer may choose the numbers to put in the brackets to fit its suitability standards.

How do you expect your income to change over the next 10 years? (check one)

☐ No change   ☐ Increase   ☐ Decrease

If you will be paying premiums with money received only from your own income, a rule of thumb is that you may not be able to afford this policy if the premiums will be more than 7% of your income.

Will you buy inflation protection? (check one)   ☐ Yes   ☐ No

If not, have you considered how you will pay for the difference between future costs and your daily benefit amount?

☐ From my income   ☐ From my savings/investments

☐ My family will pay.

> *The national average annual cost of care in [insert year] was [insert $ amount], but this figure varies across the country. In ten years the national average annual cost would be about [insert $ amount] if costs increase 5% annually.*

Drafting Note: *The projected cost can be based on federal estimates in a current year. In the above statement, the second figure equals 163% of the first figure.*

What elimination period are you considering? Number of days _____ Approximate cost $_____ for that period of care.

How are you planning to pay for your care during the elimination period? (check one)

☐ From my income   ☐ From my savings/investments

☐ My family will pay.

Questions Related to Your Savings and Investments

Not counting your home, about how much are all of your assets (your savings and investments) worth? (check one)

☐ Under $20,000   ☐ $20–30,000   ☐ $30–50,000

☐ Over $50,000

How do you expect your assets to change over the next ten years? (check one)

☐ Stay about the same   ☐ Increase   ☐ Decrease

If you are buying this policy to protect your assets and your assets are less than $30,000, you may wish to consider other options for financing your long-term care.

Disclosure Statement

☐ The answers to the questions above describe my financial situation.
OR
☐ I choose not to complete this information.
(Check one.)

☐ I acknowledge that the carrier and/or its agent (below) has reviewed this form with me including the premium, premium rate increase history and potential for premium increases in the future. [For direct mail situations, use the following: I acknowledge that I have reviewed this form including the premium, premium rate increase history and potential for premium increases in the future.] I understand the above disclosures. I understand that the rates for this policy may increase in the future. (This box must be checked)

Signed: _____

                 (Applicant)   (Date)

[I explained to the applicant the importance of completing this information.]

Signed: _____

                 (Agent)   (Date)

Agent's printed name: _____

[In order for us to process your application, please return this signed statement to [name of company], along with your application.]

[My agent has advised me that this policy does not seem to be suitable for me. However, I still want the company to consider my application.

Signed: _____

                 (Applicant)   (Date)

Drafting Note: *Choose the appropriate sentences depending on whether this is a direct mail or agent sale.*

The company may contact you to verify your answers.

Drafting Note: *When the Long-Term Care Insurance Personal Worksheet is furnished to employees and their spouses under employer group policies, the text from the heading "Disclosure Statement" to the end of the page may be removed.*

» List of State Insurance Departments, Agencies on Aging, and State Health Insurance Assistance Programs

Each state has its own laws and regulations governing all types of insurance. The insurance departments, which are listed in the left column, are responsible for enforcing these laws, as well as providing the public with information about insurance. The agencies on aging, listed in the right column, are responsible for coordinating services for older Americans. Centered below each state listing is the telephone number for the insurance counseling programs. Please note that calls to 800 numbers listed here can only be made from within the respective state.

Insurance Departments	State Health Insurance Assistance Programs	Agencies on Aging
Alabama Department of Insurance 201 Monroe Street, Suite 1700 Montgomery, Alabama 36104 (334) 269-3550 Fax: (334) 241-4192	ALABAMA (334) 242-5788 Fax: (334) 242-5594	Department of Senior Services P.O. Box 301851 770 Washington Avenue Montgomery, AL 36130–1851 1-800-243-5463; (334) 242-5743 Fax: (334) 242-5788
Alaska Division of Insurance 550 West 7th Avenue, Suite 1560 Anchorage, Alaska 99501-3567 (907) 269-7900 Fax: (907) 269-7912	ALASKA (907) 269-3669 Fax: (907) 269-3690	Division of Senior Services Department of Administration P.O. Box 110209 Juneau, AK 99811-0209 (907) 465-4879 Fax: (907) 465-4716
Office of the Governor American Samoa Government Pago Pago, American Samoa 96799 011-684-633-4116 Fax: 011-684-633-2269	AMERICAN SAMOA	
Arizona Department of Insurance 2910 North 44th Street, Suite 210 Phoenix, Arizona 85018-7256 (602) 912-8400 Fax: (602) 912-8452	ARIZONA 1-800-432-4040 Fax: (602) 542-6575	Aging and Adult Administration Department of Economic Sec. 1789 W. Jefferson - #950A Phoenix, AZ 85007 (602) 542-4446 Fax: (602) 542-6575

Insurance Departments	State Health Insurance Assistance Programs	Agencies on Aging
Arkansas Department of Insurance 1200 West 3rd Street Little Rock, Arkansas 72201-1904 (501) 371-2600 Fax: (501) 371-2629	ARKANSAS 1-800-224-6330 (501) 371-2782 (501) 371-2781	Division of Aging & Adult Services Arkansas Dept of Human Services P.O. Box 1437, Slot 1412 7th and Main Streets Little Rock, AR 72203-1437 (501) 682-2441 Fax: (501) 682-8155
California Department of Insurance 300 Capitol Mall, Suite 1500 Sacramento, California 95814 (916) 492-3500 Fax: (916) 445-5280	CALIFORNIA 1-800-434-0222 (916) 323-6525 Fax: (916) 327-208	Department of Aging 1600 K Street Sacramento, CA 95814 (916) 322-5290 Fax: (916) 324-1903
Colorado Division of Insurance 1560 Broadway, Suite 850 Denver, Colorado 80202 (303) 894-7490 1-800- 930-3745 Fax: (303) 894-7455	COLORADO 1-800- 544-9181 (888) 696-7213 (303) 894-7553 Fax: (303) 894-7455	Division of Aging and Adult Services Department of Human Services 1575 Sherman Street, Ground Floor Denver, CO 80203-1714 (303) 866-2800 Fax: (303) 866-2696
	COMMONWEALTH OF THE NORTHERN MARIANA ISLANDS	Department of Community and Cultural Affairs Civic Center Commonwealth of the Northern Mariana Islands Saipan, CM 96950 (607) 234-6011
Connecticut Department of Insurance PO Box 816 Hartford, Connecticut 06142-0816 (860) 297-3800 Fax: (860) 566-7410	CONNECTICUT (860) 424-5232 Fax: (860) 424-4966 1-800-994-9422 (in state only)	Elderly Services Division Department of Social Services 25 Sigourney St. Hartford, CT 06106 (860) 424-5277 Fax: (860) 424-5301
Delaware Department of Insurance Rodney Building 841 Silver Lake Boulevard Dover, Delaware 19904 (302) 739-4251 Fax: (302) 739-5280	DELAWARE (302) 739-6266 Fax: (302) 739-5280	Division of Services for Aging & Adults W/Physical Disabilities Dept of Health & Social Services 1901 North DuPont Highway New Castle, DE 19720 (302) 577-4791 Fax: (302) 577-4793

Insurance Departments	State Health Insurance Assistance Programs	Agencies on Aging
Dept. of Insurance & Securities Reg. Government of the District of Columbia 810 First Street NE, Suite 701 Washington, DC 20002 (202) 727-8000 x3018 Fax: (202) 535-1196	DISTRICT OF COLUMBIA (202) 496-6240 Fax: (202) 293-4043	Office on Aging One Judiciary Square 441 4th St., N.W., 9th Fl. Washington, DC 20001 (202) 724-5622 Fax: (202) 724-4979
Florida Department of Insurance State Capitol Plaza Level Eleven Tallahassee, Florida 32399-0300 (850) 413-2804 Fax: (850) 413-2950	FLORIDA 1-800-963-5337 (850) 414-2060 Fax: (850) 414-2002	Department of Elder Affairs Building B - Suite 152 4040 Esplanade Way Tallahassee, FL 32399 (850) 414-2000 Fax: (850) 414-2004
Georgia Department of Insurance 2 Martin Luther King, Jr. Drive Floyd Memorial Building 704 West Tower Atlanta, Georgia 30334 (404) 656-2056 Fax: (404) 657-7493	GEORGIA 1-800-669-8387 (404) 657-5347 Fax: (404) 657-5285	Division of Aging Services #2 Peachtree St. N.W. #36-385 Atlanta, GA 30303 (404) 657-5258 Fax: (404) 657-5285
Dept. of Revenue & Taxation Insurance Branch Government of Guam Building 13-3, 1st Floor Mariner Avenue Tiyan, Barrigada, Guam 96913 (671) 475-1843 Fax: (671) 472-2643	GUAM 1-800-586-7299	Administrator Division of Senior Citizens Dept of Public Health & Social Services Government of Guam P.O. Box 2816 Hagaina, Guam 96932 011 (671) 475-0263 Fax: (671) 477-2930
Hawaii Insurance Division Dept. of Commerce & Consumer Affairs 250 S. King Street, 5th Floor Honolulu, Hawaii 96813 (808) 586-2790 Fax: (808) 586-2806	HAWAII (808) 586-7300 Fax: (808) 586-0185	Executive Office on Aging No 1 Capitol District 250 South Hotel St., Ste 109 Honolulu, HI 96813-2831 (808) 586-0100 Fax: (808) 586-0185
Idaho Department of Insurance 700 West State Street, 3rd Floor Boise, Idaho 83720-0043 (208) 334-4250 Fax: (208) 334-4398	IDAHO S.W. 1-800-247-4422 North 1-800-488-5725 S.E. 1-800-488-5764 C. 1-800-488-5731 (208) 334-4350 Fax: (208) 334-4389	Commission on Aging 3380 Americana Terrace, Suite 120 P.O. Box 83720 Boise, ID 83720-0007 (208) 334-2423 Fax: (208) 334-3033

Insurance Departments	State Health Insurance Assistance Programs	Agencies on Aging
Illinois Department of Insurance 320 West Washington St., 4th Fl Springfield, Illinois 62767-0001 (217) 782-4515 Fax: (217) 524-6500	ILLINOIS 1-800-548-9034 (217) 785-9021 Fax: (217) 782-4105	Department on Aging 421 East Capitol Avenue Springfield, IL 62701 (217) 785-2870 Fax: (217) 785-4477
Indiana Department of Insurance 311 W. Washington Street, Suite 300 Indianapolis, Indiana 46204-2787 (317) 232-2385 Fax: (317) 232-5251	INDIANA 1-800-452-4800 (317) 233-3551 Fax: (317) 232-5251	Bureau of Aging/In Home Services 402 W. Washington St. P.O. Box 7083 Indianapolis, IN 46207-7083 (317) 232-7020 Fax: (317) 232-7867
Iowa Insurance Division 330 Maple Des Moines, Iowa 50319-0065 (877) 955-1212 (in-state only) (515) 281-5705 Fax: (515) 281-3059	IOWA 1-800-351-4664 (515) 281-6867 Fax: (515) 281-3059	Iowa Dept of Elder Affairs 200 10th St., 3rd Fl. Des Moines, Iowa 50309-3609 1-800-532-3213 Fax: (515) 242-3300
Kansas Department of Insurance 420 S.W. 9th Street Topeka, Kansas 66612-1678 (785) 296-7801 Fax: (785) 296-2283	KANSAS 1-800-860-5260 (316) 337-7386 Fax: (316) 337-6018	Department on Aging New England Building 503 South Kansas Topeka, KS 66603-3404 (785) 296-4986 1-800-432-3535 Fax: (785) 296-0256
Kentucky Department of Insurance PO Box 517 215 West Main Street Frankfort, Kentucky 40602-0517 (502) 564-6027 Fax: (502) 564-1453	KENTUCKY (502) 564-7372 Fax: (502) 564-4595	Office of Aging Services Cabinet for Health Services 275 East Main Street, 5 West Frankfort, KY 40621 (502) 564-6930 Fax: (502) 564-4595
Louisiana Department of Insurance 950 North 5th Street Baton Rouge, Louisiana 70802 (225) 342-5423 Fax: (225) 342-8622	LOUISIANA (225) 342-6334 Fax: (225) 342-7401	Office of Elderly Affairs Elderly Protective Services P.O. Box 80374, 412 N 4th St. Baton Rouge, LA 70898-0374 (225) 342-9722 Fax: (225) 342-7144
Maine Bureau of Insurance Dept. of Professional & Fin. Reg. State Office Building, Station 34 Augusta, Maine 04333-0034 (207) 624-8475 Fax: (207) 624-8599	MAINE (207) 624-5335 Fax: (207) 624-5361	Bureau of Elder & Adult Services Department of Human Services #11 State House Station Augusta, ME 04333-0011 (207) 624-5335 Fax: (207) 624-5361

Insurance Departments	State Health Insurance Assistance Programs	Agencies on Aging
	MARSHALL ISLANDS	State Agency on Aging Department of Social Services Republic of the Marshall Islands Marjuro, Marshall Islands 96960
Maryland Insurance Admin 525 St. Paul Place Baltimore, Maryland 21202-2272 (410) 468-2090 Fax: (410) 468-2020	MARYLAND 1-800-243-3425 (410) 767-1109 Fax: (410) 333-7943	Department of Aging State Office Building, Rm 1007 301 West Preston Street Baltimore, MD 21201 (410) 767-1100 Fax: (410) 333-7943
Division of Insurance Commonwealth of Massachusetts One South Station, 4th Floor Boston, Massachusetts 02110 (617) 521-7301 Fax: (617) 521-7758	MASSACHUSETTS 1-800-882-2003 (617) 222-7435 Fax: (617) 727-9368	Executive Office of Elder Affairs 1 Ashburton Place, 5th floor Boston, MA 02108 (617) 727-7750 Fax: (617) 727-6944
Office of Financial and Insurance Services State of Michigan 611 W. Ottawa St., 2nd Floor N. Lansing, Michigan 48933-1020 (517) 335-3167 Fax: (517) 373-4870	MICHIGAN 1-800-803-7174 (517) 886-0899 Fax: (517) 886-1305	Office of Services to the Aging P.O. Box 30676 Lansing, MI 48909-8176 (517) 373-8230 Fax: (517) 373-4092
Minnesota Department of Commerce 85 7th Place East, Suite 500 St. Paul, Minnesota 55101-2198 (651) 296-2488 Fax: (651) 296-4328 1-800-657-3602 www.commerce.state.mn.us	MINNESOTA 1-800-333-2433	Executive Director Board on Aging 444 Lafayette Road St. Paul, MN 55155-3843 (651) 296-2770 Fax: (651) 297-7855
Mississippi Insurance Dept 501 N. West Street Woolfolk State Office Bldg., 10th Fl. Jackson, MS 39201 (601) 359-3569 Fax: (601) 359-2474	MISSISSIPPI 1-800-948-3090 (601) 359-4929 Fax: (601) 359-9664	Council on Aging Div of Aging & Adult Services 750 N. State St. Jackson, MS 39202 (601) 359-4925 Fax: (601) 359-4370
Missouri Department of Insurance 301 West High Street, Suite 530 Jefferson City, Missouri 65101 1-800-726-7390 (573) 751-2640 Fax: (573) 526-4898	MISSOURI 1-800-390-3330 (573) 893-7900 Fax: (573) 893-5827	Division of Aging Department of Social Services P.O. Box 1337 615 Howerton Court Jefferson City, MO 65102-1337 (573) 751-3082 Fax: (573) 751-8687

Insurance Departments	State Health Insurance Assistance Programs	Agencies on Aging
Montana Department of Insurance 840 Helena Avenue Helena, Montana 59601 (406) 444-2040 Fax: (406) 444-3497	MONTANA 1-800- 332-2272 (406) 585-0773 Fax: (406) 585-0773	Office on Aging Senior Long-Term Care Division 111 Sanders Street P.O. Box 4210 Helena, MT 59604 (406) 444-7788 Fax: (406) 444-7743
Nebraska Department of Insurance Terminal Building, Suite 400 941 'O' Street Lincoln, Nebraska 68508 (402) 471-2201 Fax: (402) 471-4610	NEBRASKA 800-234-7119 (402) 471-4506 Fax: (402) 471-6559	Division of Aging Services Dept of Health & Human Services P.O. Box 95044 301 Centennial Mall-South Lincoln, NE 68509 (402) 471-2307 Fax: (402) 471-4619
Nevada Division of Insurance 788 Fairview Drive, Suite 300 Carson City, Nevada 89701-5753 (775) 687-4270 Fax: (775) 687-3937	NEVADA (702) 486-3545 Fax: (702) 486-3572	Division For Aging Services Department of Human Resources 3416 Goni Road, Building D-132 Carson City, NV 89706 (775) 687-4210 Fax: (775) 687-4264
New Hampshire Insurance Dept 56 Old Suncook Road Concord, NH 03301 (603) 271-2261 Fax: (603) 271-1406	NEW HAMPSHIRE (603) 271-3944 Fax: (603) 271-4643	Department of Insurance Division of Elderly & Adult Services State Office Park South Brown Building - 129 Pleasant St. Concord, NH 03301-3857 (603) 271-4394 Fax: (603) 271-4643
New Jersey Department of Insurance 20 West State Street CN325 Trenton, New Jersey 08625 (609) 292-5360 Fax: (609) 984-5273	NEW JERSEY (609) 943-3378 Fax: (609) 943-4033	Division of Senior Affairs Department of Health & Senior Services P.O. Box 807 Trenton, NJ 08625-0807 (609) 943-3345 Fax: (609) 943-3343
New Mexico Department of Insurance PO Drawer 1269 Santa Fe, New Mexico 87504-1269 (505) 827-4601 Fax: (505) 476-0326	NEW MEXICO 1-800-432-2080 (505) 827-7640 Fax: (505) 827-7649	Michelle Lujan-Grisham, Director State Agency on Aging La Villa Rivera Bldg 228 East Palace Avenue, Grd Fl. Santa Fe, NM 87501 (505) 827-7640 Fax: (505) 827-7649

Insurance Departments	State Health Insurance Assistance Programs	Agencies on Aging
New York Department of Insurance 25 Beaver Street New York, New York 10004-2319 (212) 480-2292 Fax: (212) 480-2310	NEW YORK 1-800-333-4114 (518) 473-5108 Fax: (518) 486-2225	Office for the Aging Two Empire State Plaza Albany, NY 12223-1251 (518) 474-5731 Fax: (518) 474-1398
North Carolina Dept. of Insurance PO Box 26387 Raleigh, North Carolina 27611 (919) 733-3058 Fax: (919) 733-6495	NORTH CAROLINA 1-800-443-9354 (919) 733-0111 Fax: (919) 733-3682	Division of Aging 2101 Mail Service Center 693 Palmer Drive (Fedex only-zip 27603) Raleigh, NC 27699-2101 (919) 733-3983 Fax: (919) 733-0443
North Dakota Dept. of Insurance 600 E. Boulevard Bismarck, North Dakota 58505-0320 (701) 328-2440 Fax: (701) 328-4880	NORTH DAKOTA 1-800-755-8521 (701) 328-2977 Fax: (701) 328-4880	Aging Services Division Department of Human Services 600 South 2nd St., Suite 1C Bismarck, ND 58504 (701) 328-8910 Fax: (701) 328-8989
Ohio Department of Insurance 2100 Stella Court Columbus, Ohio 43215-1067 (614) 644-2658 Fax: (614) 644-3743	OHIO 1-800-686-1578 (614) 644-3399 Fax: (614) 752-0740	Department of Aging 50 West Broad Street - 9th Fl Columbus, OH 43215-5928 (614) 466 5500 Fax: (614) 995-1049
Oklahoma Department of Insurance 2401 NW 23rd St., Suite 28 Oklahoma City, Oklahoma 73107 (405) 521-2828 Fax: (405) 521-6635	OKLAHOMA 1-800-763-2828 (405) 521-6628 Fax: (405) 522-4492	Aging Services Division Department of Human Services P.O. Box 25352, 312 N.E. 28th St Oklahoma City, OK 73105 (405) 521-2327 Fax: (405) 521-2086
Oregon Insurance Division 350 Winter Street NE, Room 440 Salem, Oregon 97301-3883 (503) 947-7980 Fax: (503) 378-4351	OREGON 1-800-722-4134 (503) 947-7984 Fax: (503) 378-435	Seniors and People With Disabilities 500 Summer St . NE, E13 Salem, OR 97301-1073 (503) 945-5811 Fax: (503) 378-8966
	PALAU	State Agency on Aging Department of Social Services Republic of Palau P.O. Box 100 Koror, Palau 96940

Insurance Departments	State Health Insurance Assistance Programs	Agencies on Aging
Pennsylvania Insurance Dept 1326 Strawberry Square, 13th Fl Harrisburg, Pennsylvania 17120 (717) 783-0442 Fax: (717) 772-1969	PENNSYLVANIA 1-800- 783-7067 (717) 783-8975 Fax: (717) 772-2730	Department of Aging Forum Place 555 Walnut Street, 5th Fl Harrisburg, PA 17101-1919 (717) 783-1550 Fax: (717) 772-3382
Puerto Rico Dept of Insurance Cobian's Plaza Building 1607 Ponce de Leon Avenue Santurce, Puerto Rico (787) 722-8686 Fax: (787) 722-4400	PUERTO RICO (787) 721-8590 Fax: (787) 721-6510	Governors Office For Elderly Affairs P.O. Box 50063 Old San Juan Station San Juan, PR 00902 (787) 721-6121 Fax: (787) 721-6510
Rhode Island Insurance Division Dept. of Business Regulation 233 Richmond Street, Suite 233 Providence, Rhode Island 02903-4233 (401) 222-2223 Fax: (401) 222-5475	RHODE ISLAND (401) 462-0508 Fax: (401) 222-2130	Department of Elderly Affairs John O. Pastore Center, Benjamin Rush (Bldg. #55) 35 Howard Avenue Cranston, RI 02920 (401) 462-3000 Fax: (401) 462-0503 TTY: (401) 462-4000
South Carolina Dept. of Insurance 300 Arbor Lake Drive, Ste 1200 Columbia, South Carolina 29223 (803) 737-6160 Fax: (803) 737-6229	SOUTH CAROLINA 1-800-868-9095 (803) 898-2850 Fax: (803) 898-4513	Dept of Health & Human Services P.O. Box 8206, 1801 Main St. Columbia, SC 29202-8206 (803) 898-2501 Fax: (803) 898-4515
South Dakota Division of Insurance Dept. of Commerce & Reg 118 West Capitol Avenue Pierre, South Dakota 57501-2000 (605) 773-3563 Fax: (605) 773-5369	SOUTH DAKOTA (605) 773-3656 Fax: (605) 773-6834	Office of Adult Services & Aging 700 Governors Drive Pierre, SD 57501 (605) 773-3656 Fax: (605) 773-6834
Tennessee Dept. of Commerce & Insurance. Davy Crockett Tower, Fifth Fl 500 James Robertson Parkway Nashville, Tennessee 37243-0565 (615) 741-2241 Fax: (615) 532-6934	TENNESSEE 1-800-525-2816 (615) 741-4955 Fax: (615) 253-1159	Commission on Aging Andrew Jackson Building 500 Deaderick Street, 9th Fl. Nashville, TN 37243-0860 (615) 741-2056 Fax: (615) 741-3309
Texas Department of Insurance 333 Guadalupe Street Austin, Texas 78701 1-800-252-3439 Consumer Help (512) 463-6464 Fax: (512) 475-2005	TEXAS 1-800-252-9240 Fax: (512) 305-7463	Department on Aging 4900 North Lamar, 4th Fl Austin, TX 78751-2316 1-800-252-9240 (512) 424-6840 Fax: (512) 424-6890

Insurance Departments	State Health Insurance Assistance Programs	Agencies on Aging
Utah Department of Insurance 3110 State Office Building Salt Lake City, Utah 84114-1201 (801) 538-3800 Fax: (801) 538-3829	UTAH (801) 538-3910 Fax: (801) 538-4395	Division of Aging & Adult Services Department of Human Services Box 45500, 120 North - 200 W. Salt Lake City, UT 84145-0500 (801) 538-3910 Fax: (801) 538-4395
Vermont Division of Insurance Dept. of Banking, Ins. & Sec. 89 Main Street, Drawer 20 Montpelier, Vermont 05620-3101 (802) 828-2900 Fax: (802) 828-2949 Consumer Service: 1-800-631-7788	VERMONT (802) 241-4425 Fax: (802) 241-2325	Aging and Disabilities 103 South Main Street Waterbury, VT 05671-2301 (802) 241-2400 Fax: (802) 241-2325
Attn.: Marileen Thomas #18 Kongens Gade, Charlotte Amalie St. Thomas, Virgin Islands 00802 (340) 774-7166 Fax: (340) 774-9458 or (340) 774-6953	VIRGIN ISLANDS (340) 778-6311 x2338 Fax: (340) 778-5500	Senior Citizen Affairs Department of Human Services #19 Estate Diamond Fredericksted St. Croix, VI 00840 (340) 692-5950 Fax: (340) 692-2062
State Corporation Commission Bureau of Insurance Commonwealth of Virginia PO Box 1157 Richmond, Virginia 23218 (804) 371-9694 Fax: (804) 371-9873	VIRGINIA 1-800- 552-3402 (804) 662-7048 Fax: (804) 662-9354	Department for the Aging 1600 Forest Avenue Preston Building, Suite 102 Richmond, VA 23229 (804) 662-9333 Fax: (804) 662-9354
Washington State Office of the Insurance Commissioner 14th Avenue & Water Streets PO Box 40255 Olympia, Washington 98504-0255 (360) 586-7515 Fax: (360) 586-3535	WASHINGTON 1-800-397-4422 (206) 654-1833 Fax: (206) 389-2745	Aging & Adult Services Admin Department of Social & Health Services P.O. Box 45050 1115 Washington Street, SE Olympia, WA 98504-5050 (360) 902-7797 Fax: (360) 902-7848
West Virginia Dept. of Insurance PO Box 50540 Charleston, West Virginia 25305-0540 (304) 558-3354 Fax: (304) 558-0412	WEST VIRGINIA 1-800-642-9004 (304) 558-3317 Fax: (304) 558-5609	Bureau of Senior Services 1900 Kanawha Blvd, East Holly Grove-Building 10 Charleston, WV 25305-0160 (304) 558-3317 Fax: (304) 558-5609

Insurance Departments	State Health Insurance Assistance Programs	Agencies on Aging
Office of the Commissioner of Insurance State of Wisconsin 121 E. Wilson Madison, Wisconsin 53702 (608) 267-1233 Fax: (608) 261-8579	WISCONSIN 1-800-242-1060	Bureau of Aging & LTC Resources Department of Health and Family Services One West Wilson St. P.O. Box 7851 Madison, WI 53707-7851 (608) 266-2536 Fax: (608) 267-3203
Wyoming Department of Insurance Herschler Building 122 West 25th Street, 3rd East Cheyenne, Wyoming 82002-0440 (307) 777-7401 Fax: (307) 777-5895	WYOMING 1-800-856-4398 (307) 856-6880 Fax: (307) 856-4466	Aging Division 6101 Yellowstone Road, 259B Qwest Building Cheyenne, WY 82002 1-800- 442-2766 (307) 777-7986 Fax: (307) 777-5340

≫ Key Terms

Key terms are indicated in the text by boldface and this symbol ▣▬ in the margin. Key terms are introduced, defined, and explained on the page or pages listed below.

Index

>> Frequently Asked Questions About the AHIP Examination

What material is covered in the examination for the AHIP course *Long-Term Care, Part I*?

The 13 chapters of the textbook *Long-Term Care: Understanding Needs and Options* (Second Edition).

Is information from appendices covered in the exam?

No. The appendices are provided as a resource for the reader. Any information that appears *only* in the appendices (and not in the chapters of the text as well) is not tested.

How many questions are on the exam, and how much time do I have?

There are 75 questions. You have two hours. (Some test formats have fewer questions. Inquire with the person who will be conducting your exam.)

What is the format of the exam questions?

All questions are multiple choice.

EXAMPLE ▶ *Mrs. Conway lives in her own apartment, but in the building are available such services as three meals a day, help with housekeeping and laundry, and assistance with personal care and medications. This is an example of what type of long-term care?*

> *a. Adult day center.*
> *b. Assisted living.*
> *c. Hospice care.*
> *d. Respite care.*

(The correct answer is b.)

Some questions are multiple-option multiple choice.

EXAMPLE ▶ *Which of the following are activities of daily living?*
I. Bathing.
II. Dressing.
III. Using the telephone.

a. I and II only
b. I and III only
c. II and III only
d. I, II, and III

(The correct answer is a.)

A few questions are application questions. These require you to determine which of the facts given in the question are relevant and then apply your knowledge to reach a conclusion.

EXAMPLE ▶ *Mrs. Jacobs has a long-term care insurance policy with a daily benefit of $100, a benefit period of three years, an annual premium of $1,200, and a shortened benefit period nonforfeiture option. After ten years, she stops paying premiums. If in the future she meets one of the policy's benefit triggers, she will be entitled to*

a. one year of benefits.
b. $12,000 of benefits.
c. $3,600 of benefits.
d. no benefits.

(The correct answer is b.)

You should be able to answer the question by applying your knowledge of how different nonforfeiture options work.

Are there questions on the statistics and numbers in the textbook?

Yes, but not very many. For a few simple and important numbers, the exact figure must be known. For example, Medicare does not pay any benefits for nursing home care after 100 days. The student would be expected to know this number.

Usually, however, an approximate idea of the number is sufficient. For example, the text reports that in 2004 the average cost of a semiprivate room in a nursing home in the United States was about $169 per day. The student would not be expected to know this exact figure, but she should know approximately how much nursing home care costs. An exam question might ask, for instance, whether the average daily cost of a semiprivate room is about $80, $120, $170, or $220.

Is information from tables covered in the exam?

Yes, information from the tables found in the 13 chapters is covered, but exam questions focus on the main points, not details. For example, Table 3.1, "NAIC Guidelines for Viatical Payments," lists the percentage of the death benefit paid for each of several life expectancy ranges. The student would not be asked the percentage paid for each range; instead, she would be expected to know that the lower the life expectancy, the higher the percentage.

If I can answer all the review questions, will I be able to pass the exam?

Not necessarily. The review questions are intended to help the student learn the most fundamental concepts and information, but they do not cover everything that might be asked on the exam.

I have a lot of experience in insurance. Can I pass the exam without reading the textbook or studying?

Possibly, but you should be aware that the examination is based on the most common practices in the insurance industry. What your company does may differ. The safest approach is to read the textbook and see if you know the material. This will go very quickly if you already have a lot of knowledge.

» AHIP's Courses and Professional Designations

For more than 40 years, the Insurance Education Program of America's Health Insurance Plans has offered current, comprehensive, and economically priced courses for professionals seeking to gain a greater knowledge and understanding of the health insurance industry. Since 1958, more than 500,000 people have enrolled in these courses. Many are employees of health insurance plans, but consultants, third-party administrators, agents, brokers, and other health insurance professionals also study with us. In addition, many noninsurance professionals, including health care providers, economists, consumer advocates, and government officials, take AHIP courses to learn more about the operations of our industry and advance their careers in their own fields.

Courses include:

- The Fundamentals of Health Insurance (two courses)
- Medical Expense Insurance
- Supplemental Health Insurance
- Managed Care (three courses)
- Disability Income Insurance (three courses)
- Long-Term Care Insurance (four courses)
- Health Care Fraud (three courses)
- Medical Management (six courses)
- HIPAA Rules, Requirements, and Compliance (two courses)
- Customer Service
- Dental Benefits

The completion of AHIP courses leads to widely respected professional designations:

- Health Insurance Associate (HIA®)
- Managed Healthcare Professional (MHP)
- Disability Income Associate (DIA)

- Disability Healthcare Professional (DHP)
- Long-Term Care Professional (LTCP)
- Health Care Anti-Fraud Associate (HCAFA)
- Medical Management Associate (MMA)
- HIPAA Associate (HIPAAA)
- HIPAA Professional (HIPAAP)
- Healthcare Customer Service Associate (HCSA)

Health Insurance Associate (HIA®)

The HIA® designation, offered since 1990, is held by more than 19,500 professionals. It signifies that the holder has acquired a broad knowledge of health insurance products and health plan operations. Designees have a solid understanding of insurance principles and terminology, contracts, underwriting and pricing, sales and marketing, policy administration, claims administration, cost management, regulation, and health care fraud and abuse. They are familiar with a variety of health coverages, including medical expense insurance, disability income insurance, long-term care insurance, and supplemental products such as hospital indemnity coverage, specified disease insurance, Medicare supplements, accident coverage, and dental plans.

Managed Healthcare Professional (MHP)

The MHP designation was established in 1996, and there are now more than 6,300 designees. Professionals with the MHP are knowledgeable about the latest developments in health care management as well as the operations of traditional health insurance. They have acquired an understanding of the structure and operation of managed care organizations, provider contracting and provider relations, network administration, member services, claims administration, and quality assurance, as well as marketing, rating, financing, and budgeting. They are also familiar with regulatory policies and processes, the accreditation of managed care organizations, and the role of health care management in government health benefit programs.

Disability Income Associate (DIA)

Holders of the DIA designation have an in-depth understanding of how an injury or illness can lead to a substantial financial loss and how disability income (DI) insurance can protect against this risk. Designees are knowledgeable about employer-sponsored disability programs, ranging from sick leave benefits to long-term disability income plans, and about federal and state government disability programs, including Social Security Disability Insurance, workers' compensation, and state temporary disability income programs. They also understand how individuals can supplement these employer- and government-sponsored programs with private DI insurance. Finally, DIA designees are familiar with the role DI insurance plays in retirement, estate, and long-term care planning.

Disability Healthcare Professional (DHP)

In the DHP designation program, students move beyond the specialized course of study of the DIA program to expand their understanding of the health insurance industry. DHP designees have the same in-depth knowledge of disability income (DI) insurance as DIA holders, including employer-sponsored benefits, government programs, individual DI policies, and retirement, estate, and long-term care planning. But they also have a familiarity with the principles of insurance, other health coverages, and the role DI insurance plays in the larger health insurance field.

Long-Term Care Professional (LTCP)

The LTCP program is an exciting opportunity for insurance professionals who want to learn about the increasing need for long-term care, the various ways of financing it, and the growing role of long-term care insurance. Students in the program learn about long-term care services, settings, and providers; they explore financing options such as personal savings, government programs, reverse mortgages, and annuities, discovering the limitations of each; and they examine in detail long-term care insurance, including policy provisions, underwriting and pricing, sales and marketing, policy administration, claims administration, and regulation. LTCP designees have the expertise they need to succeed in this expanding field.

Health Care Anti-Fraud Associate (HCAFA)

The HCAFA program provides those working in health insurance plan anti-fraud units and others with the information and skills they need to detect and prevent health care fraud and abuse. HCAFA designees understand how common fraudulent schemes work and how they can be discovered and investigated. They are familiar with many types of fraudulent activity, including fraud perpetrated by providers, consumers, agents, and health plan employees, as well as fraud involving a wide variety of health coverages, including medical expense insurance, managed care, disability income insurance, long-term care insurance, and others. Finally, holders of the HCAFA designation are knowledgeable about the laws and enforcement tools that can be used to stop fraud.

Medical Management Associate (MMA)

The MMA program is designed for employees of health insurance plans who seek a deeper understanding of medical management and its impact on the insurance industry, as well as for health care providers, third-party administrators, and others whose businesses and practices are affected by it. The six courses of the program cover in depth the main branches of medical management: utilization management, case management, disease management, quality management, and call centers. Students also learn about legislative and regulatory requirements and accreditation and certification, and they explore emerging trends in this rapidly evolving field.

HIPAA Associate (HIPAAA)

The HIPAA Associate designation signifies that a person has acquired a basic working knowledge of the administrative simplification provisions of the Health Insurance Portability and Accountability Act of 1996 (HIPAA), with a focus on the Privacy Rule. The program covers HIPAA terminology; organizational roles and responsibilities; policies and procedures; required documents, such as the privacy notice, business associate agreement, and authorization; patients' and individuals' rights; and guidelines on uses and disclosures of protected health information. By expanding their knowledge of compliance issues and HIPAA's impact on business and clinical practices, those earning the HIPAAA designation will be better positioned to help their organizations develop the policies and procedures required by this complex law.

HIPAA Professional (HIPAAP)

The HIPAA Professional designation is for those who plan to assume the role of HIPAA privacy official. As with the HIPAA Associate program, students learn about the policies, procedures, and documents required by the Privacy Rule as well as the rights of individuals and guidelines for the use and disclosure of information. HIPAAP designees supplement this basic grounding with more detailed study of HIPAA security standards and the measures that must be adopted to ensure the privacy and integrity of health data.

Healthcare Customer Service Associate (HCSA)

To stay competitive in today's environment, providers of health care services and products must offer outstanding customer service. The HCSA designation program helps people from all parts of the health care industry improve their relationships with internal and external customers and enhance the performance of their organizations. Students in the HCSA program acquire proven strategies for solving customer service problems; learn the basics of training, hiring, and managing customer service staff; and discover ways to achieve quality service and create customer-driven organizations.

For more information
visit our web site (www.insuranceeducation.org)
or call 800-509-4422.

» AHIP Insurance Education Books

» Health Insurance

The Health Insurance Primer: An Introduction to How Health Insurance Works

This book, together with *Health Insurance Nuts and Bolts* (below), serves as a complete introduction to the health insurance field. The authors assume no prior knowledge and begin by explaining basic concepts and terminology, but they progress to an in-depth examination of such topics as the various kinds of health insurance, health insurance contracts, underwriting, and sales and marketing. *The Health Insurance Primer* is an excellent choice for beginners in the industry and those from other fields who need a basic understanding of health insurance. (Study manual included.)

Health Insurance Nuts and Bolts: An Introduction to Health Insurance Operations

The introduction to the fundamentals of group and individual health insurance begun in *The Health Insurance Primer* continues in *Health Insurance Nuts and Bolts*. Topics include policy issue, renewal, and service; claims administration; pricing health insurance products; managing the cost of health care; government regulation; and fraud and abuse. (Study manual included.)

Medical Expense Insurance

For those who have a basic grounding in the principles and functioning of health insurance, this book provides a more detailed look at the most common kind of health insurance in America—medical expense insurance. The text begins by describing the two coverages that provide health benefits to most Americans: group major medical insurance and individual hospital-surgical insurance. Subsequent chapters discuss contract provisions, underwriting and pricing, sales and marketing, policy administration, claims administration, and industry issues. (Study manual included.)

Supplemental Health Insurance

This book provides those with a basic understanding of health insurance and supplemental health insurance with more detailed information about the major supplemental products in the marketplace. These include hospital indemnity coverage, specified disease insurance, Medicare supplements, accident coverage, dental plans, and prescription drug plans. For each product, the text points out the gaps in basic health insurance that create the need for additional coverage and explains how the product meets that need and protects the individual from financial risk. (Study manual included.)

» Managed Care

Managed Care: What It Is and How It Works (Second Edition)

Completely updated and expanded by Peter R. Kongstvedt, MD, the foremost authority in the field, this new edition provides readers with a clear and easy-to-follow introduction to the fundamental concepts and basic functioning of health care management. It covers the origins and evolution of managed care, the various types of managed care organizations, network management, medical management, regulation, accreditation, and other topics. An extensive glossary of managed care terms is included. This book serves as the text for the AHIP course Managed Care, Part A. (Study materials available online.)

Managed Care: Integrating the Delivery and Financing of Health Care, Part B

The second book in AHIP's health care management series builds on the basic knowledge the student acquired in the introductory course, with a focus on operational issues and problems. It discusses in greater depth the governance and management structure of managed care organizations; selective medical provider contracting; network administration and provider relations; marketing and member services; claims administration; financing, budgeting, and rating; legal issues; accreditation; and regulation. (Study manual included.)

Managed Care: Integrating the Delivery and Financing of Health Care, Part C

Part C of this series explores a variety of topics. It describes the continued evolution of health care management, including the impact of regulation and consumer attitudes. It examines the role managed care plays in government health benefit programs, such as Medicare, Medicaid, and health benefit plans for federal employees and military personnel. The functioning of managed care in specialty areas, such as pharmacy, dental, behavioral health, and vision benefits, is discussed. Finally, ideas are offered on how the operations of managed care organizations can be improved. (Study manual included.)

Dental Benefits: A Guide to Dental PPOs, HMOs, and Other Managed Plans (Revised Edition)

In this expanded and updated edition, Donald S. Mayes provides a comprehensive survey of managed care in the field of dental benefits. He explains how managed dental benefit plans function and how they differ from medical managed care plans. He describes the structure of managed dental plans, with a focus on the two main types, dental PPOs and HMOs. Several other topics, including cost issues and plan management, are discussed, and tools for evaluating and comparing dental plans are provided. This book serves as the text of an elective course in the MHP designation program.

» Disability Income Insurance

Disability Income Insurance: A Primer

Many people are unaware of the major financial loss that can result from a long-term disability, or they mistakenly believe that government programs will cover this loss. This book analyzes the financial risk of disability; it describes Social Security disability insurance, workers' compensation, and other government programs and makes clear why they do not provide adequate benefits for most people; and it explains how disability income (DI) insurance *can* provide sufficient benefits. Employer-sponsored group DI coverage is briefly described (it is fully covered in the third book of this series), while individual DI insurance is examined in detail, with a focus on underwriting, contract provisions, and claims administration. (Study materials incorporated into text.)

Disability Income Insurance: Advanced Issues

The second book in the AHIP disability series explores more complex issues, including structuring DI benefit programs to meet the needs of lower, mid-tier, and higher-level employees; combining group and individual DI coverage; implementing executive bonus and salary continuation plans; and coordinating DI insurance with both tax-qualified and nonqualified retirement plans. Specialty products, such as disability overhead expense insurance, key-person DI insurance, and disability buyout insurance, are described. Students also learn about the important role of DI insurance in planning for retirement, long-term care needs, and estate protection. (Study materials incorporated into text.)

Disability Income Insurance: Group and Worksite Issues

Many people look to their employers as the source of disability benefits, and many employers choose group disability income insurance as the best means of providing these benefits. In this book, the reader finds comprehensive and up-to-date information on all aspects of group DI insurance, including product design and policy features, underwriting and pricing, sales and marketing, and claims administration. A related product, voluntary worksite plans, is also examined, and regulatory and tax considerations are discussed. (Study materials incorporated into text.)

» Long-Term Care Insurance

Long-Term Care: Understanding Needs and Options

As people live longer and the population ages, there is an increasing need for home health care, assisted living, nursing home care, and other forms of long-term care. This book provides an introduction to the field of long-term care and long-term care insurance (LTCI). It begins with an explanation of what long-term care is, who needs it, and how and where it is provided. It then looks at several ways of paying for long-term care and the limitations of each. It examines long-term care insurance, describing how it works and explaining why it is often the best solution to the problem. Finally, it discusses the ways salespeople and insurance company personnel can bring this solution to the people who need it. (Study materials incorporated into text.)

Financing Long-Term Care Needs: Exploring Options and Reaching Solutions

Long-term care services can be very expensive, and if they are required for more than a few months the total cost can represent a significant financial burden. But by planning ahead, the average person can provide for his or her long-term care needs. This second volume of AHIP's long-term care series examines in greater detail the various ways of meeting the need for long-term care. It looks at personal savings and assets, family support, Medicaid, reverse mortgages, commercial and private annuities, life insurance, and both individual and group long-term care insurance. The advantages and disadvantages of each of these is discussed, giving the reader a clear understanding of the role each can play in long-term care planning. (Study materials incorporated into text.)

The Long-Term Care Insurance Product: Policy Design, Pricing, and Regulation

Long-term care insurance (LTCI) is a relatively new and still evolving product. This book looks at this evolution, focusing on the innovations insurers have made to better meet consumer needs and on the impact of regulation, especially HIPAA. It also provides a comprehensive look at LTCI policies, covering benefit eligibility, benefit amounts, inflation protection, elimination periods, policy maximums, nonforfeiture, renewal, lapse, and other features. Other topics include premium calculation, group long-term care coverage, and the relation of long-term care insurance to other insurance products. (Study materials incorporated into text.)

Long-Term Care Insurance: Administration, Claims, and the Impact of HIPAA

The administration of long-term care insurance continues to evolve as the product itself develops. This book looks at practices and procedures in several administrative areas, including underwriting, issuance, premiums, policy maintenance, policyholder services, and reporting. It describes the long-term care claim process and the steps insurers take to control claim costs and hold down premium prices. In addition, the impact of the Health Insurance Portability and Accountability Act of 1996 (HIPAA) is discussed. (Study materials incorporated into text.)

» Health Care Fraud

Health Care Fraud: An Introduction to Detection, Investigation, and Prevention

Every year, fraud and abuse add billions of dollars to our country's health care expenditures. This book describes how health care fraud is perpetrated and what is being done to combat it. It explains how some of the most common fraudulent schemes operate, how these schemes can be detected and investigated, and the laws that can be brought to bear against them. Fraud perpetrated by health care providers, consumers, and others is covered, and although medical expense insurance fraud is emphasized, fraud involving managed care and disability income insurance is also included. (Study materials incorporated into text.)

Insurance Fraud in Key Products: Disability, Long-Term Care, MedSupp, Drug Coverage, & Others

While the first book in AHIP's fraud series focuses on medical expense insurance, the second looks at a range of health insurance products: disability income insurance; long-term care insurance; dental, behavioral health, and prescription drug benefits; and Medicare supplement insurance. Fraud in two nonhealth coverages, life insurance and property/casualty insurance, is also discussed. For all of these products, common fraudulent schemes are examined, and legal and investigative issues are explored. (Study materials incorporated into text.)

Legal Issues in Healthcare Fraud and Abuse: Navigating the Uncertainties (Second Edition)

This book, written by Carrie Valiant and David E. Matyas and published by the American Health Lawyers Association, provides those working to combat health care fraud with the legal background relevant to investigations, civil actions, and criminal prosecutions. It surveys the major players in anti-fraud enforcement and examines in detail the most important laws and regulations. Topics include anti-kickback legislation, restrictions on physician self-referrals, false claims and fraudulent billing, exclusion from federal health benefits programs, fraud and abuse in managed care, state anti-fraud laws, legal representation issues, and many others. (Study materials available online.)

» Medical Management

Medical Management: An Overview

The introductory text of this six-part series provides readers with a background in the development of managed care and an overview of its latest phase—medical management. Early models of managed care, current practice, and emerging trends are discussed. Readers learn why and how health care benefit plans are developed, how legislative and regulatory requirements affect the industry, and how accreditation and certification function to promote quality. (Study materials incorporated into text.)

Medical Management: Utilization Management

The purpose of utilization management is to determine whether health care services are medically necessary and appropriate. It seeks to ensure that the treatment, provider, and facility that best meet a patient's needs are chosen. This book describes utilization management's evolution and explores its future. The reader acquires an understanding of the goals of utilization management, the programs and organizations that have adopted it, the professionals who are responsible for it, the processes they use to implement it, and the tools and resources they need to support it. (Study materials incorporated into text.)

Medical Management: Call Centers

This book presents an overview of the "telehealth" industry—from standard call centers that serve health plan members to more sophisticated systems that provide access to registered nurses who can assist patients with specific health problems. Readers are given practical pointers on how to establish a call center, select vendors, hire and train employees, and maintain quality in customer service. They learn about legal and regulatory requirements and look at trends in the use of electronic communications in health care. (Study materials incorporated into text.)

Medical Management: Case Management

Case managers help patients and their families navigate health care delivery systems and manage their own health care needs. Practitioners come from many disciplines—they are nurses, social workers, rehabilitation counselors, and physicians—and they collaborate with other stakeholders to achieve quality, cost-effective outcomes. This book gives the reader a clear understanding of the basic concepts, goals, and processes of case management; the professionals and organizations in the field and the services they provide; legal, ethical, and risk management concerns; and emerging trends. (Study materials incorporated into text.)

Medical Management: Disease Management

Disease management is a system of coordinated health care interventions for a medical condition in which patient education and self-care are key components. This book takes a practical approach to the subject and offers plenty of substance to readers at all levels, from beginners seeking a basic understanding to managers of disease management programs. Topics include the history of disease management, current challenges, and future projections; model programs for specific diseases; the tools and techniques used in these programs; regulatory and legislative issues; and accreditation and certification programs. (Study materials incorporated into text.)

Medical Management: Quality Management

Providing the right health care at the right time in a way that produces the most favorable patient outcomes is the objective of quality management. This book covers the essentials, helping students understand why quality management is important, how programs are implemented, and who the key stakeholders are. It introduces students to the fundamental framework of quality management, providing an overview of the programs, processes, and procedures used by health care organizations to ensure the delivery of quality services. (Study materials incorporated into text.)

» HIPAA

HIPAA Primer: An Introduction to HIPAA Rules, Requirements, and Compliance (Second Edition)

Who must comply with HIPAA? What does "protected health information" mean? What types of information must be protected? This practical guide to the Privacy Rule of the Health Insurance Portability and Accountability Act of 1996 (HIPAA) provides the answers to these questions and many more. It explains what the rule is, what its key components are, and whom it affects. It discusses key concepts such as covered entities, business associates, and the minimum necessary standard and offers examples of their real-life application. A glossary of HIPAA terminology is also included.

HIPAA Action Items for Insurers

This practical workbook provides clear guidelines that will help insurance company managers and personnel interpret the HIPAA Privacy Rule and implement compliance. It includes an easy-to-understand description of the essential elements of the Privacy Rule; an outline of compliance tasks, such as appointing a privacy official and training personnel; scenarios and case studies that show how HIPAA requirements apply in the insurance industry; and templates for creating compliance documents such as the privacy notice, business associate agreement, and authorization. (Study materials incorporated into text.)

» Customer Service

Customer Service Strategies for the Health Care Environment

In an easy-to-read style, this book offers strategies, tools, and exercises designed to make health care employees more aware of customer service issues and create a customer-driven organization. A wide range of topics is covered, including removing the barriers to excellent customer service; improving communication with customers; assessing the quality of customer service; analyzing service cycles; hiring, training, and managing personnel; and handling customer complaints. Many valuable resources are included, such as 50 expert tips for quality customer service and provocative self-study quizzes in each chapter. (Study materials available online.)

These books may be ordered
by calling 1-800-828-0111.

» The AHIP Insurance Education Program

Gregory F. Dean, JD, CLU, ChFC, LTCP
Executive Director

Joyce C. Meals
Deputy Director, Education

Letitia Faison
Deputy Director, Finance

Leanne Dorado
Registrar and Manager of Education Operations

Kevin Gorham
National Accounts Manager

Matthew Grant
Internet Services Coordinator

Wanda Ellison
Administrative Assistant/CE Coordinator

Charlene Burger
Administrative Assistant/CE Coordinator